# Times and Places

*by* WILLIAM S. GRAY

*and* MAY HILL ARBUTHNOT

BASIC READERS : CURRICULUM FOUNDATION SERIES

*A Revision of the Elson-Gray Basic Readers*

Scott, Foresman and Company

CHICAGO ATLANTA DALLAS NEW YORK

# Contents

## Young Citizens of Today

PAGE

Return of the Puddle Duck......HUBERT EVANS.......... 8

Whiskers Steals the Show.......ELEANOR HAMMOND...... 16

Star Pupil.....................MABEL F. RICE.......... 25

Betsy Finds a Way.............DOROTHY CANFIELD FISHER 33

How Andy Helped His Team.....IRIS MAY KNIGHT........ 43

## Young Citizens of Early Days

Going West....................ENID MEADOWCROFT...... 52

The Long Journey..............ENID MEADOWCROFT...... 58

The Neighborhood Needle.......ZELIA WALTERS......... 67

Hasty Pudding.................CORNELIA MEIGS........ 74

Susanna Jane's Secret.........ESTHER COOPER......... 85

A Boy and His Book............ALICE E. ALLEN........ 94

Wool Gathering................DELIA M. STEPHENSON.... 99

Steam Comes Upriver...........JOSEPHINE E. PHILLIPS....106

# Wonders of Our Times

PAGE

Radio Rescue . . . . . . . . . . . . . . . JOSEPHINE PEASE . . . . . . . 116

Messages from the Sea . . . . . . . . . ALICE DALGLIESH . . . . . . . 122

Steam Shovels Are Handy . . . . . . STERLING NORTH . . . . . . . . 129

Southbound Flight . . . . . . . . . . . . ADA N. CAMPBELL . . . . . . . 140

A New Job for a Tractor . . . . . . . LAWRENT LEE . . . . . . . . . . 149

When the Lights Failed . . . . . . . . CHARLES P. BURTON . . . . . . 158

# Story-Land of Here and Now

The Wizard of Vilville . . . . . . . . . . CAROL JOHNSTONE SHARP . . 168

The Huckabuck Family . . . . . . . . . CARL SANDBURG . . . . . . . . . 182

The Princess Who Could Not Cry . ROSE FYLEMAN . . . . . . . . . . 188

Three and Three . . . . . . . . . . . . . . CHALLIS WALKER . . . . . . . 196

King Peramund's Wish . . . . . . . . . EDWARD WADE DEVLIN . . . . 202

# Young Citizens of Other Lands

At Home in Any Language . . . . . . MARIA MARTIN . . . . . . . . . . 212

The Red-Brimmed Hat . . . . . . . . . ELIZABETH KENT TARSHIS . 217

Adventure in Guatemala . . . . . . . . MARIAN CANNON . . . . . . . . 228

A South American Visit . . . . . . . . ALICE DALGLIESH . . . . . . . . 239

Mario's Pet . . . . . . . . . . . . . . . . . ESTHER G. HALL . . . . . . . . . 244

Christmas in Alaska . . . . . . . . . . . ALLEN CHAFFEE . . . . . . . . 253

# The Great Outdoors

A Camp in the Canyon . . . . . . . . . ELIZABETH PALMER . . . . . . . 264

Bushy Tail's Escape . . . . . . . . . . . GALL AND CREW . . . . . . . . . 274

The Partridge Family . . . . . . . . . . ERNEST THOMPSON SETON . 282

A Wild Colt's Lesson . . . . . . . . . . PAUL BROWN . . . . . . . . . . . 289

Gray Wing and Nika . . . . . . . . . . . WILLIAM H. BUNCE . . . . . . 294

Smoozie the Reindeer........... ALMA SAVAGE........... 304
The Polar Bear Twins.......... JANE TOMPKINS......... 312
Johnny's Alligator............. IDELLA PURNELL........ 320

## Famous People of Other Times

Joseph and His Brothers........ BIBLE................. 330
David the Shepherd Boy........ BIBLE................. 344
Saint George.................. HISTORICAL SOURCES..... 353
Joan of Arc................... HISTORICAL SOURCES..... 360

## Old Tales from Everywhere

Chanticleer and the Fox........ CHAUCER............... 372
A Barber's Discovery.......... LA FONTAINE FABLE..... 381
The Seven Dancing Stars....... INDIAN LEGEND......... 385
Rumplestiltskin............... GRIMM................. 390
   *Adapted by Walter de la Mare*
The Ugly Duckling............. HANS CHRISTIAN ANDERSEN 404
The Golden Eggs............... AESOP FABLE........... 415
Cinder Lad................... NORSE TALE............ 419

# Young Citizens of Today

# Return of the Puddle Duck

"Let's go for a boat ride," Sam Black said to his sister. "I'm tired of swimming."

"We can't," Jane answered as she followed Sam through the water to the sandy beach in front of their summer cottage. "It's that new boy's turn to use the boat. You know Captain Bill said we had to share it with him. We had our turn this morning."

Jane was right, but that didn't make Sam feel any happier. He and Jane had been the only ones to use Captain Bill's rowboat, the Puddle Duck. Now that Peter Duncan had come to Pelican Lake, they had to share it.

As Sam pulled on his sweater, he glanced longingly at the dock where the Puddle Duck had been bobbing up and down in the shallow water. Suddenly he gave a loud whistle.

"Look!" he cried, his eyes fastened on an object out in the deeper water beyond the dock. "What happened to the Puddle Duck?"

Jane shaded her eyes with her hand as she spied the moving object in the water. The Puddle Duck was no longer tied to the dock. The wind was blowing the boat straight toward the rocks beyond the point.

The rowboat was too far out for them to swim to it. If they only had a car! Then they could reach the point in time to save the boat. They could wade into the shallow water and pull it to safety before the wind sent it on the rocks.

"Quick!" Sam called excitedly. "We'll get Captain Bill and his truck." Off they raced down the beach toward the Captain's house.

As he raced along, the awful thought came to Sam that perhaps he had forgotten to tie the boat. But he was sure he remembered knotting the rope and pulling it tight. That was a rule everyone remembered—just like staying out of the water right after eating or not going swimming alone.

"Maybe you didn't tie the boat," cried Jane.

"Of course I tied the Puddle Duck," Sam burst out. "I'm no baby. I know the rules. I've never broken them yet."

Suddenly an idea flashed into his mind. Peter Duncan was new at the lake. Peter hadn't heard the rules every summer. So it would be easy for him to forget just once. And forgetting the rule just once would be enough to wreck the Puddle Duck.

The thought of having no more good times in the boat made Sam quicken his stride. He dashed to the Captain's house in a final burst of speed that left Jane far behind.

"Captain! Captain Bill!" Sam shouted as soon as he could get his breath. He pounded on the door and shouted again.

There was no answer.

In less than a minute Jane caught up with Sam and spied a note high on the door over Sam's head.

"Look!" she exclaimed. "There's a note!"

Quickly they read the two short sentences in Captain Bill's big handwriting.

"Gone to village. Be back about five."

"What can we do now, Sam?" Jane asked in a helpless tone.

Sam tried to think of a plan, but only one thought came to his mind. Peter Duncan had left the boat untied. So Peter would have to do something to keep it from being wrecked.

"Come on," Sam said gruffly. "Let's get Peter Duncan right away."

They found the new boy lying in a swing on his front porch. "The Puddle Duck is loose," Sam called out, without even waiting to say hello. "Did you forget to tie it?"

Peter sat up quickly at Sam's words, and his face wore a puzzled frown. "I didn't use the boat at all," he said in a surprised voice. "I was ready to go rowing, but I cut my foot on some broken glass, and I've been here ever since."

11

Sam's mind was in a whirl. If the new boy hadn't been near the Puddle Duck, then Sam himself must have left the boat untied.

Then Jane's voice broke into his puzzled thoughts. "The Captain has gone to town," she was saying to Peter. "We read a note he left on his door. We have to get him and get him quick!"

"Got a bike?" Peter questioned.

Sam shook his head. "No, but I can ride one pretty well."

"Take my bike, then," Peter said quickly. "If you're speedy enough, you can catch the Captain before the Puddle Duck reaches the rocks."

Sam was off in a flash, scarcely waiting for Peter to finish speaking.

As Sam wheeled up to the village store, the Captain was just coming out, his arms full of bundles.

"The Puddle Duck's loose," Sam shouted. "It's near the rocks beyond the point."

Captain Bill didn't waste any time at all. He tossed his bundles into the waiting truck. "Up with your bike," he ordered, and the bicycle followed the bundles into the truck.

As the roaring motor grew less noisy, Sam explained what had happened.

"Did the new boy have the boat?" Captain Bill asked as they rounded the point at full speed and headed for the beach.

"No, sir. I had it last," Sam said, though he knew that breaking the rule might mean no more rides in the Puddle Duck.

13

As the truck rattled and bumped to a stop, Sam could see the old Puddle Duck bobbing closer and closer to the brown rocks. The water here was shallow enough for wading, but the sharp rocks were dangerous.

"We didn't get here one minute too soon," Captain Bill said, pulling off his shoes.

Sam was still barefooted. Without waiting for the Captain, he splashed into the water and waded out to the boat. Quickly he shoved it away from the rocks. Then he climbed aboard, and with steady strokes of the oars he guided the boat away from the rocks and up to the beach.

Captain Bill reached for the rope hanging from the bow of the Puddle Duck and pulled the boat up on the sand.

"Shall we load it on the truck, Captain?" Sam asked slowly. He was thinking that a vacation without the Puddle Duck wouldn't be much fun.

For a moment the Captain didn't answer. He kept looking at the rope in his hand.

"You tied up the Puddle Duck, all right," he said at last. "Look."

Sam looked. The rope was knotted about the very piece of wood to which he had tied it that morning. But the old bent nails that held the wood to the dock had pulled loose. The Puddle Duck had run away all by itself. The mystery was solved.

Sam was too happy to speak clearly.

"Then I—I—didn't—," he stammered.

Captain Bill chuckled. "No, Sam. You didn't break the rule. Your knot is still tied. If anybody broke a rule, I did. I should have noticed those loose nails weeks ago.

"Stay aboard the Puddle Duck and row it home. Any boy who saves a boat from being wrecked surely has a right to use it."

As Sam guided the rowboat toward the dock, he saw Jane and Peter waiting there. Suddenly Sam had an idea. He and Jane wouldn't need to wait while Peter used the boat. They could all use it together. That would be sharing it as much as taking turns.

"Hi!" he called to the two on the dock. "Here's the Puddle Duck, safe and sound. Let's all go rowing."

# Whiskers Steals the Show

## Plans for a Circus

For two weeks the Boy Scouts in Greenfield had been practicing for their circus. It was not going to be any small back-yard circus that cost only two pins to see. It was to be just like a real circus, with Scamp, Jim Post's pet bear cub, as star performer.

There were no lions or elephants, but they had a trick pony, a trained police 'dog, and several other animals. They even had a Punch and Judy puppet play as a side show.

The circus was to be held Saturday afternoon in the field behind Mr. Swift's barn.

The boys had sold over a hundred tickets at ten cents for children and twenty-five cents for grown-ups. The money from the tickets was going to the Red Cross, and so the grown people were willing to help. A big crowd was expected.

Then on the day before the circus Tommy Swift and Jim Post quarreled. At the last minute Tommy wanted to use Whiskers, his old white goat, as a circus performer.

"But Whiskers is no good at tricks," Jim argued. "And there isn't time to train him now."

"It won't matter whether Whiskers knows any real tricks or not," Tommy answered. "He'll look funny in the parade. I'm going to fix up my old cart for him to pull. And I can dress up in fancy Halloween clothes and tie a clown hat on Whiskers' head. I might paint his face like a clown's, too."

Jim sniffed. "Whiskers will never stand for all that," he insisted. "That old goat will just run away and butt somebody with those long horns of his and spoil the show."

"He will not!" Tommy argued heatedly.

The more the two angry boys argued, the more determined each one was to have his own selfish way.

"I don't care," Tommy said finally. "The circus is being given on my father's land, isn't it? I guess I can have my own goat on our own land. If I can't have Whiskers in the circus, you can't use our field for the show—so there!"

"Well, if you're determined to have that goat in the show, I'll take Scamp and my bike out of it!" Jim shouted stubbornly.

Three other Scouts rushed up and tried to settle the quarrel before their Scoutmaster heard of it.

"Look here, fellows," Bill Woodburn said. "We mustn't let a quarrel spoil our circus. We've sold a lot of tickets, and it wouldn't be honest to give the show and not make it just as good as we can. Besides, we want all the money we can get for the Red Cross, don't we?"

Jim and Tommy felt very much ashamed of themselves. Yet each was still determined to have his own way.

That evening Tommy went out to the barn and practiced secretly with Whiskers.

Saturday arrived clear and bright, with the promise of a perfect circus day. The Scouts spent a busy morning at the field, trying to arrange everything in order.

Pens and cages had to be arranged around the fence for a tame opossum, some rabbits, a pet gray squirrel, and two green parrots. A "Fierce Wild Monster," that looked very much like Ricky Parker's old raccoon, was put in one cage. A "Dog-faced Monkey," that barked like Bob Long's dog, was in another.

Tim Brown practiced walking on his stilts until he was sure his act would be perfect. The other boys wrapped popcorn balls and made lemonade to sell.

At exactly two o'clock the dozen young performers, with stilts, bicycles, trick pony, and the bear cub, waited in the barn for the signal to begin.

Then the band started up. To the sound of tooting tin horns and thumping drums, the performers paraded into the ring behind Bill Woodburn, the ringmaster.

19

Around the ring marched the performers, as the audience clapped and cheered loudly.

Bob Long did his tumbling act perfectly. Tim Brown's stilt-walking act was excellent. The pony shook hands and rolled over at his master's order. Duke, the police dog, did every clever trick he had learned in the city police department.

"La—dies and gentlemen!" the ringmaster announced, cracking his long whip. "You will now be entertained with a bicycle-riding act by the celebrated bear, Scamp, and his daring young trainer, Jim Post."

## The Hit of the Show

Meantime Jim was making arrangements for his stunt. Scamp, the bear cub, allowed himself to be placed on the handlebars of Jim's bicycle, and now the star act of the circus was about to begin.

At the same time Tommy was behind the barn, where he had hidden Whiskers.

"Here's one stunt that will surprise even the ringmaster," Tommy chuckled to himself as he pulled his grandmother's ruffled white nightgown over his suit.

Whiskers, hitched to a small two-wheeled cart, stood patiently while his master tied a clown hat under his chin.

"Jim says you aren't smart enough to do tricks!" Tommy whispered as he patted the goat. "He'll see that you can entertain an audience as well as any circus animal."

Tommy picked up the reins and drove to the performers' entrance just as Jim entered the ring with Scamp on the handlebars.

The ringmaster almost dropped his whip as he stared at the unexpected performers. He could scarcely believe his eyes.

At the sight of the strange figures, Scamp leaped from the handlebars. Jim struggled to keep his bicycle upright, but he was helpless. The fat cub's leap was too much for him. In a second the bicycle and its rider were tumbling on the grass, and Scamp was waddling away with frightened squeals.

"Whoa, Scamp, whoa!" Jim yelled, as he scrambled to his feet and sped after the cub.

Scamp saw only the crowded rows of people surrounding the ring. He kept running in a circle instead of dashing for the open aisle to the gate. Jim whirled after him.

At that instant another runaway happened. Whiskers, frightened and excited by all the noise, gave a start that threw Tommy out on the ground. Away Whiskers sped, with the empty cart rattling behind him. Tommy jumped to his feet and tore after the goat, trying to clutch the dragging reins.

Round and round the ring—once, twice, a third time—the boys and animals whirled. Tommy felt ashamed of himself. Why had he tried such a foolish thing? Now he had spoiled Jim's act. His lower lip quivered a little. Then suddenly he realized that the audience liked the wild chase. They were stamping and clapping and yelling.

There were shouts of "Hi, Scamp!"

"Run, Whiskers, old fellow!"

"Hurrah for Tommy!"

Tommy decided to act as if it had all been meant to happen the way it did. He stopped chasing Whiskers and bowed this way and that in answer to the roars of delight.

Just then Whiskers turned suddenly, breaking loose from the cart. For a half-second he glared at his master with angry eyes. Then he lowered his head and charged at the strange-looking figure in white.

Tommy doubled up with a wild yell and tumbled to the ground. Whiskers cleared him in one leap and left the circus ring at a gallop. Tommy picked himself up, just as Jim clutched his cub firmly by the collar.

"Whew!" Jim breathed, as the two boys headed for the barn. "That was some stunt, Tommy! I'm sorry I talked that way about Whiskers. He's the hit of the show."

Tommy felt his ears redden. "That stunt wasn't what I planned," he admitted in an ashamed tone. "I'm sorry I spoiled your act. But Whiskers made a pretty good clown."

"He certainly did!" Jim exclaimed. "He gave the audience a big surprise."

"And me, too," Tommy agreed with a mischievous grin. "In more ways than one!"

## Star Pupil

"Oh, Miss Brand!" called Jean Martin eagerly as she burst into the schoolroom one autumn morning. "Here's a new pupil. She's nine years old, and she can't speak a word of English!"

The teacher looked up from her desk and saw Jean leading forward a brown-eyed girl with long braids of shining black hair.

"Good morning," said Miss Brand, looking at the shy new girl with a friendly smile. "Can you tell us your name?"

The girl did not answer, but looked from Jean to the teacher with questioning eyes.

"She doesn't even *understand* English," explained Billy Mains, who had come into the room behind the two girls. "She's just moved here from Mexico. Her name is Rosa. She lives two doors from me."

"Rosa! That's a pretty name," Miss Brand said as she led the new pupil to a desk. "Try to say your name. Say Rosa."

The girl's dark eyes seemed to brighten as she heard the familiar name, but she made no reply.

"Say Rosa," repeated Miss Brand, shaping the words carefully with her lips.

Still no answer. There was only that shy, questioning look from the Mexican girl.

"Say Rosa," the teacher said again. She did not raise her voice, but each word was spoken clearly.

At last Rosa seemed to understand that something was expected of her.

"Say Rosa," she said slowly, each word a perfect echo of the teacher's clear voice.

In the meantime nearly all the pupils had come into the room, and they smiled at Rosa's unexpected reply.

From the pleasant looks on their faces, Rosa thought that she must have said something clever.

"Say Rosa. Say Rosa. Say Rosa," she echoed happily.

"You'll have to teach her English, Miss Brand," one of the boys exclaimed.

Miss Brand shook her head. "You mean *we* shall have to teach her English," she said with a smile. "There are forty of you, and I shan't have much time for all your lessons if I have to teach Rosa by myself. But you can all help me.

"Now get the flag, so that we can start the morning with the pledge of allegiance."

Billy took the big flag from its place in the corner and held it high while the children saluted the flag and repeated the pledge of allegiance. Then the pupils sang "America." Rosa listened eagerly to all the unfamiliar and queer-sounding words.

After the song was finished, Miss Brand said, "Before we start our own lessons, let's think how we can help Rosa learn to speak English."

27

Robert Hall had his hand up first. "We'd better start with easy words," he suggested. "A word for something she can see, like a book." He picked up his reader, pointed to it, and said clearly, "Book."

Rosa only stared at him and said nothing. The others caught Robert's idea now, and Tommy held up his arithmetic.

"Book. Say book," he repeated.

"Don't use the word *say*," Jean warned. "She thinks it's a part of every word."

Tommy nodded to show that he understood and tried again. "Book."

Rosa had been watching closely. Now she glanced around the room as if searching for something. Suddenly she jumped up, ran to the front of the room, and placed both hands on the teacher's dictionary.

"Book," she exclaimed, laughing excitedly.

The whole class clapped their hands and cheered. Rosa was learning English!

"She ran to the dictionary," Robert said. "Let's teach her the word *run*."

"Go ahead," smiled the teacher.

Robert pointed to Tommy and said, "Run!" Tommy ran to the blackboard at top speed.

"Run!" ordered Robert, pointing to Jean, and Jean raced to the dictionary. Then he pointed to Rosa and gave the command to run. But Rosa did not move an inch.

"We must try again," Robert said with a frown of disappointment. So Tony, Susan, and Wilfred all ran at Robert's command. Then he pointed to Rosa.

"Run," he called out. And this time Rosa ran to the window, her long braids flying, while the class yelled with excitement.

"Maybe we could teach her the difference between *run* and *walk*," suggested Ellen, as the class quieted down.

"Walk, Robert," she said, and he walked to the dictionary, moving with careful steps.

"Run," called Ellen, and Robert raced back to his desk in double-quick time.

As Ellen called out the commands, several other boys and girls walked or ran about the room. When Rosa's turn came, she repeated each command to prove that she knew the difference between them.

"That's fine," Miss Brand said, placing her hand gently on Rosa's dark braids.

Rosa seemed to understand and beamed with pleasure as she admiringly patted the teacher's bright red dress.

"She likes red," said Jean eagerly. "May we teach her just one more word? May we teach her the word *red?*"

Miss Brand nodded, and Jean patted the teacher's dress, saying, "Red."

Rosa jumped up quickly and held out her own dark brown dress. "Red," she echoed, and looked around for approval. But the pupils' smiles turned to frowns. Here was a new problem. Rosa thought *red* meant *dress*. How could they teach her the difference?

"I have red socks," Jean said. She pointed to them, clearly repeating the word *red*.

Robert took a shiny red apple from his desk. "Red," he said with a friendly grin.

The boys and girls looked around for more red objects. But Rosa was quicker than they were. She raced to the flag in the corner and pointed to a bright red stripe.

"Red," she declared proudly, as the class clapped its approval of her success.

Then Miss Brand asked the pupils to get out their arithmetic books, and Rosa's first English lesson was over.

As the days went by, Rosa proved to be a good pupil. She learned to read easy stories, she learned to count by using marbles, and soon she was learning to solve arithmetic problems. The children proudly called her their star pupil and were as pleased as Rosa at her success.

Finally it came time to make arrangements for the last day of school. Everyone in the class was to take part in a program, and all the parents and friends were invited. In the meantime the class talked over the problem of finding a part in the program for Rosa.

"Let her say the pledge of allegiance," Robert suggested. "That will show everyone she's a real citizen of our country now."

The class agreed at once. So did Rosa. She said the pledge over and over until she knew every word.

When it was time for Rosa's part in the program, she walked quickly to the stage. Her heart was pounding under her scarlet dress, but she was no less excited than her forty proud teachers.

The class scarcely breathed while Rosa saluted the flag and began to speak.

"I pledge allegiance to the flag of the United States of America . . . ."

Slowly but clearly Rosa went on speaking the familiar words until the whole pledge of allegiance to the United States was finished. The children beamed at each other in delight. Their teaching had been successful. Their star pupil had learned her lesson perfectly.

# Betsy Finds a Way

### A Change in Plans

Betsy was celebrating her birthday at the County Fair. She had come with her friends, the Wendell family, who lived on the next farm. And of course Betsy's little friend, Molly, had come along.

The two girls were allowed to wander about until noon, entertaining themselves by seeing the sights. They had forty cents to spend, but all they bought was a five-cent glass of lemonade apiece.

At noon they met Mr. and Mrs. Wendell at their car, and they all had a picnic lunch under a big oak tree.

As they ate, the girls chattered happily about the merry-go-round, the balloon-seller, and the popcorn and lemonade booths.

The Wendells were already tired of sight-seeing, and so they said they were going home earlier than they had planned.

Betsy's face showed her disappointment.

"Would you like to stay and go home with the Vaughans?" Mrs. Wendell asked. Both girls agreed that this would be great fun.

"All right, then, girls," said Mrs. Wendell. "Will Vaughan is working in a popcorn booth over by the merry-go-round. We'll ask him what time his family is going home."

But when they got to the booth, a strange young man was there. "Isn't Will Vaughan working here?" asked Mrs. Wendell.

"He'll be here later," said the young man. "Will's turn is from two to four."

"Now, Betsy," said Mrs. Wendell, "you'll have to come to Will's booth at two o'clock and ask what time the Vaughans are going to start home. Don't keep them waiting."

"Oh, we'll meet them on time," promised Betsy, as she and Molly started off.

Betsy and Molly still had thirty cents out of the forty they had brought with them. Now the two girls put their heads together to see how they would spend the six nickels.

Molly wanted a red balloon. While they were buying that, a man came along selling toy dogs with curly tails. Betsy bought one done up neatly in a box.

Now they had fifteen cents left, and they decided to have a ride apiece on the merry-go-round. But glancing up at the clock in the tower of a tall building, Betsy noticed that it was almost two o'clock. So she decided to go at once and find out the exact time the Vaughans would start home.

She found the booth, but Will Vaughan was not in it, nor was the other young man. Instead there was a new man who told them that the Vaughans had heard bad news. One of their cows had hurt itself, and so they had gone home in a great rush.

Betsy snatched Molly's plump little hand. "Hurry!" she cried, almost breathless with fear. "We must find the Wendells before they get away."

## Left Behind

Betsy dragged Molly as fast as the child's short, fat legs would go to the space where the Wendells' car had been parked.

But the Wendells had gone!

Betsy's heart seemed to leap up in her throat and choke her. She almost burst into tears with disappointment. They were twelve miles from home, and neither she nor Molly could walk that far. They had just fifteen cents left, and the only people they knew in all that crowd had gone.

"What can we do, Betsy?" Molly wailed.

Betsy choked back her own sobs and put her arms about her wailing friend. She wiped away the tears and said, "Now, Molly, stop crying. I'll get you home all right. I always find a way to do what I have to do."

"How?" wailed Molly helplessly, as sobs choked her throat.

"Never mind how," said Betsy, although her lower lip quivered a little. "Let's go back to the popcorn booth, Molly. Perhaps Will Vaughan didn't go home after all."

But when they came to the booth again, the man told them Will Vaughan had left.

"We had planned on going home with the Vaughans," murmured Betsy in a low tone.

"Looks as though you'll have to go home on a bus or train," said the man.

"Does——it cost much to go to Hillsboro?" stammered Betsy, her voice quivering.

"I don't know what a bus ticket costs," the man said. "But you can ride on the train for half price at twenty cents apiece. There's a train to Hillsboro at six o'clock."

"We have only fifteen cents," said Molly.

Betsy looked at her silently for a moment and then declared, "I'll earn the rest! I'll have to! There isn't any other way!"

But how could she do it? How could a ten-year-old girl earn money at a county fair?

The girls wandered on. Molly was not at all worried now. She knew Betsy would take care of everything. But Betsy was anxious. No one seemed to need her help.

Three o'clock came, then three-thirty, and Betsy had not yet earned the price of the two tickets. Although they were walking slowly, she kept feeling breathless and choked.

Suddenly she heard a weary voice from a booth murmuring, "Oh, if I could only rest for an hour, I'd feel much better."

Betsy turned quickly. Here was someone needing help. A tired-looking woman, who had lemonade and cookies to sell, was talking to a friend in the next booth.

The weary voice went on, "I think I could manage if I had only the selling to do, but I've a whole panful of lemonade glasses that must be washed."

"Oh, oh, please!" stammered a small voice. "I'll do it all for twenty-five cents."

"Do what, child?" asked the tired woman, glancing down at the eager girl who stood at her elbow.

"Everything!" said Betsy. "I'll wash those glasses and sell cookies and lemonade. Then you can go out and rest. I'll work until five o'clock for twenty-five cents."

The woman stared at Betsy in surprise. "A little girl like you!" she exclaimed.

"I'm ten years old today," said Betsy, "and I can wash dishes as well as anybody."

"Yes, I think she can," said the friend in the next booth. "And I'm sure that she can sell lemonade, too. She looks honest and seems to have plenty of pluck."

The woman waited no longer. She tied an apron around Betsy's waist, gave her a few directions, and left, saying she would be back at five o'clock.

## Betsy Proves Her Pluck

Betsy began to wash and wipe the dozens of dirty glasses. Never in her life had she thought she would just *love* to wash dishes.

"It's all right, Molly! It's all right!" she said cheerfully. But Molly only nodded and climbed up on a stool where she could watch the holiday crowd go by.

Then business began for Betsy.

"Two cookies, please," said a man. He laid down a nickel, took two cookies, and turned away. Sure enough, a sign tacked on the booth gave the price as "2 for 5."

A lady with a boy was the next customer. She gave Betsy two nickels and one dime to pay for two glasses of cold lemonade and four cookies. Business was getting better.

As Betsy arranged a row of glasses along the counter, she looked anxiously at the clock in the tower across the way. It was nearly five. What if the woman should oversleep?

But at the stroke of five the woman came back, looking fresh and greatly rested.

"Here is a quarter for you," she said, "and now have some cookies." Then she gave each girl a double handful.

"Thank you so much!" said Betsy. "We can eat them on the train."

The girls left the booth, but Betsy rushed back to say, "Several customers came and bought things. The money is on the shelf."

Betsy and Molly hurried out the gate of the fairgrounds into the main street of the town and down to the station. Betsy pushed her quarter and three nickels into the ticket-seller's window and said in a firm, clear voice, "Two tickets to Hillsboro, please."

When she actually held the precious bits of paper in her hand, her knees shook so that she had to sit down until the train came. Drawing a long, deep breath, she slowly ate a cookie. All of a sudden she felt very tired.

She was still tired when they got out of the train at Hillsboro and started wearily up the road to the farm. Molly dragged her feet as she walked, and Betsy put her arm about the younger child's waist.

A car was coming toward them. So the girls moved aside and stood waiting until the road should be clear again.

When the driver saw them, he stopped with a loud shout. It was Betsy's uncle! Now they wouldn't have to walk any farther.

He ran up to them, calling anxiously, "Are you all right?"

"Why, yes," said Betsy. "We're all right. We came home on the train."

When Betsy told how she had earned the quarter, her uncle took out a handkerchief and blew his nose loudly.

"Whew!" he said. "I do declare! You're the pluckiest girl in the whole county."

# How Andy Helped His Team

## Andy's Promise

"Hello," called a boy's pleasant voice as Andy Waters went skating down Oak Street.

"Hi, there," shouted Andy, saluting his new neighbor, Philip Turner. "Want to go skating?"

"I can't," Philip answered. "I lost my roller skates last fall, and I haven't saved enough money to buy another pair."

"That's hard luck, Philip," said Andy. "If you had skates, you could be in the skating race next Saturday."

"Skating race? Who's in it?"

"Some boys from Lincoln School," Andy explained. "We have two teams with five on each side. My team is the Tigers. The other team is the Cubs."

"Say," cried Philip. "That sounds great."

"You see," Andy went on explaining, "the losing team has to treat the winning team to a picnic. We're all meeting on Pine Street to practice. I'll have to go now, but you may use my skates some day. Good-by."

As Andy skated off, he heard Philip call, "Thanks! I'll be glad to use your skates."

Andy thought it was a shame that Philip was lonely. But he had moved there since school had closed for the Easter holidays, and the other boys weren't acquainted with him.

At the corner Andy was met by his cousin, Nick Brown, who was captain of the Tigers. "It's time you got here! We were just going to start without you," Nick scolded.

"Say, Nick," Andy said, "that new boy looks sort of lonesome. Couldn't we use him on our team?"

"Of course not, Andy," declared Nick. "The Cubs have only five on their team. It's too late for them to get another skater."

"I hadn't thought of that," Andy replied.

So for a time Philip was forgotten. Andy practiced hard during the holidays, for his heart was set on having his own team win. The Cubs had won the last two races. Andy couldn't help knowing that it was partly his fault, since his short legs kept him from being a fast skater.

One day Nick said to him, "That Cub team has some long-legged skaters. It's a shame you can't skate faster, Andy."

Just then Philip Turner came along and watched the Tigers skate past. Andy gave him a shamefaced smile, for he remembered his promise to let Philip use his skates.

"After this race is over, I'll let Philip use them all he wants to," Andy told himself. "He has the long legs of a good skater."

Suddenly Andy thought of a way to help his own team win, and also to help Philip get acquainted with the other boys.

That evening after practice Andy ran over to the home of his new neighbor.

"Hello, Phil," he said. "I have something important to talk over with you. But first would you like to try my roller skates?"

"Oh, would I!" cried Philip in a delighted voice, as he fastened on the skates.

Andy watched Philip as he sped toward the corner and back with long, even strokes.

"It's great to be on skates once more!" said Philip, his eyes shining.

"How would you like to take my place in the race tomorrow?" Andy asked suddenly.

"Do you mean that? Honest?" said Philip, looking very much astonished.

"Yes, of course," answered Andy. "You're a faster skater than I am. My legs are too short. The Tigers must win, and if you take my place, we'll have a better chance."

"But what will your captain say?"

"Never mind that," replied Andy. "If our team wins, he won't care."

## An Exciting Race

Saturday morning at ten o'clock nearly all of the boys who were to be in the race were at their meeting place, the big vacant lot on Pine Street. Each Cub wore a red arm-band above his left elbow, and each Tiger wore a yellow arm-band with black stripes.

Mr. Herbert, the Scoutmaster, who was to be the starter, had already arrived. A crowd of pupils from Lincoln School stood about the vacant lot, waiting to see the race.

"Why hasn't Andy come?" asked Nick. "We're going to start in a few minutes."

Just then Andy and Phil came running up.

"Nick, I'm not going to skate," Andy began quietly. "I've made arrangements for Phil to take my place."

"What's the matter, Andy? Have you hurt yourself?"

"No, but I've decided not to skate."

Nick and the other Tigers were astonished.

"Got cold feet, did you?" teased one of the boys, grinning at Andy.

Andy's face turned red. "Why, no," he answered pleasantly, in spite of the teasing. "But Philip Turner is a better skater than I am. He's going to take my place."

Captain Nick took Andy aside. "Come on, Andy," he begged. "You're just *giving* the race to the Cubs. That new boy can't skate."

"Yes, he can," Andy insisted. "Wait and he'll prove it. I know he'll help us win."

Just then Mr. Herbert shouted, "First pair
of skaters, ready on the starting mark."

Each Tiger was lined up with a member of
the other team who was about his own size,
for only two boys were to race at a time.
The first two boys set their toes on the starting line. Then Mr. Herbert blew his whistle,
and they were off.

At first the boy on the Cub team took the
lead, but the Tiger skater was not far behind.

When they reached the turn at the end
of the block, the Tiger began to gain on the
Cub skater. Faster and faster he went, while
all the boys and girls shouted. A moment
later he darted across the finish line ten
feet ahead of the other boy.

At the end of four rounds, each team had won twice. The fifth round would decide the race, and Philip Turner was the fifth skater for the Tigers.

"Don't forget that I'm counting on you. I know you can do it," Andy said, as Phil took his place on the starting mark.

The Cub who was to skate against Philip was about the same size, although Philip's legs were longer. Then for the fifth time came the starting signal.

"On your mark!" cried Mr. Herbert.

"Get set!" And he blew the whistle.

At first Philip dashed ahead. The Tigers cheered and yelled until their throats were aching. Suddenly their cheers changed to hopeless groans. Philip's skate had caught in a crack, and down he went, full-length on the sidewalk.

The Cub skater darted quickly ahead, and by the time Philip was on his feet again, the other boy had gained a big lead.

"Go it, Phil!" shouted Andy. "You have a chance to beat him yet!"

The Tigers stopped groaning and began to cheer. Philip was creeping up on the Cub. Both boys skated the full length of the block, made a quick turn, and came speeding back toward their cheering teams.

The Cub racer was still ahead, but Philip kept gaining until the two were side by side.

Now they were near the finish. Everyone was shouting, but Andy's excited voice was heard above all the others.

"You can do it, Phil! You can do it!"

Philip put all his strength into the last few yards and crossed the finish line just ahead of the Cub skater. The Tigers had won!

"Philip can easily get acquainted now," Andy thought happily as both teams cheered for the new boy at the tops of their voices. Andy yelled loudest of all, for his skates had actually won the race, even if another boy had been wearing them.

# Young Citizens
# of Early Days

# Going West

"We're going West," announced Mrs. Burd one morning. "Father has sold the farm, and we're leaving as soon as we can get ready. We're going with Will Matthews, who has a big covered wagon for the journey."

"West!" exclaimed Andy and Jonathan in excitement. But Sally looked anxious.

"Are there Indians out West?" she asked.

"Yes, plenty of them," Mrs. Burd replied. "But there were Indians right here when my grandfather settled on this farm. If my grandmother wasn't afraid of them, I guess I won't be. Nor you either, Sally Burd."

"You see, Sally," said her father, slicing a large loaf of bread, "we just can't raise

enough on our farm here to pay for all the things we need. But along the Ohio River there is good rich land that is very cheap. President Washington needs people to help settle that part of the United States. Out West we can build a new home, and I can make a better living for us all."

The next few weeks were busy ones indeed, and then the day came to start the journey. Sally was up long before daybreak. She had been helping her mother for two hours when she woke Andy and Jonathan.

"Get up," she said. "The wagon is here, and Mother wants to pack these quilts."

The two boys dressed hurriedly and dashed out. There in the dim light of early morning stood a huge, white-topped wagon. Jonathan clutched Andy's elbow in excitement.

"It's a real covered wagon," exclaimed Jonathan. "And look at those horses."

"Yes," said Andy. "Aren't they fine?"

So they were! There were four of them—beautiful, strong gray horses.

Their heavy black harness was shiny, and over each horse's collar was hung a bell. The bells jingled merrily as the animals tossed their heads and stamped the ground, eager to start away.

Mr. Burd was already loading the wagon, and Mr. Matthews was helping him. They came out of the house, dragging a big leather trunk, just as the boys turned and saw them.

"Can we help you?" Andy asked, darting forward.

It was just at this moment that Mrs. Burd called from the barn, "Jonathan and Andy! Come here! I need you."

The two boys ran and found their mother tugging with all her strength at a big bag.

"What's in the bag?" asked Andy.

"Three rosebushes and a lilac bush," his mother answered. "I dug them up last night. There's plenty of earth around them to keep them fresh. So they ought to live."

The bag was heavy and awkward, but at last they tucked it away in the wagon.

Mr. Burd took from his pocket a list he had made many days ago and began to check over the things they wanted to take.

"Plow, shovel, crowbar, hoe, saw, ax, pick, and the box of tools. Seed for planting, spinning wheel, wooden butter churn, leather trunk, pots, kettles, dishes, quilts, tubs, pillows, featherbeds, rocking chair, clock, bed, one oak dresser—"

He stopped hopelessly and said, "We can't possibly take everything on this list. We'll have to store the bed and dresser in the barn until we can send for them."

After much pushing, tugging, and groaning the remaining things on the list were loaded. "There!" said Father. "Now for breakfast."

Just as they finished eating, the house was suddenly filled with people who had come to say good-by. Granny Burd was there, and Uncle Dan, and friends from miles around who wanted to wish them luck.

At last, somehow, they were aboard the big wagon. Andy and Jonathan sat in the back, their dog between them, while the others clambered up in front. Will Matthews picked up his reins and cracked his long whip.

All four horses moved forward. The great wheels turned, and the folks were actually on their way.

"Good-by, good-by!" called everyone, and Uncle Dan shouted, "Good luck, folks! Next year I'll join you and buy some cheap land out West myself."

Suddenly Sally felt her eyes fill with tears as she realized she was leaving the only home she had ever known. "Oh," she murmured with a sob, "I don't want to go."

"Stop that, Sally Burd," said her mother, choking back her own tears as she spoke. "Don't you dare let Father see you cry."

Then she put her arm around her daughter. "Remember this, Sally," she said, "we can't go back. We must keep our chins up. We are pioneers now."

# The Long Journey

### In the Covered Wagon

On toward the west went the pioneers, the big wagon jerking from side to side on the narrow, rough road. At noon, when the sun was just overhead, Will Matthews drove to the side of the road and stopped.

"Time to eat," he announced. So everyone stood around and ate ham and cheese and cold corn bread with jam on it. There were cookies and apple pie, too. Then Sally unpacked cups, and each one had a drink from a spring of clear water beside the road.

The two men fed and watered the horses. They examined the horses' feet to see that no shoes had come loose, tightened up the harness, straightened the heavy collars, and greased a squeaky wagon wheel.

When everyone felt fresh and rested, they continued the journey.

The afternoon went quickly for Sally and the boys. They were astonished when Father announced they were stopping for the night.

A few minutes later Mr. Matthews turned off the road and guided the horses carefully through the pine trees, near the bank of a creek. He and Mr. Burd unhitched the horses, while the boys opened a bag of grain and fed the four hungry and weary beasts.

Will Matthews and Jonathan carried pails to the creek for water. Mr. Burd and Andy got wood and made a campfire. Mrs. Burd put six big potatoes in the fire to roast and sliced some bacon, while Sally undid a bundle of dried strawberry leaves and put them in boiling water to make some tea.

Not long after the meal was finished, they prepared for sleep. Mother and Sally spread a fat featherbed and some quilts under the wagon seat for their bed. But the boys and men rolled up in blankets under the trees.

Next day was much like the first. They went about fifteen miles and camped out at night. Then it rained, and for a week they traveled only five or six miles a day.

At length they came to the mountains, and crossing them was the hardest part of all. At times the Burds struggled over a road so steep that it seemed as if the horses were going straight up and might fall over backward. Then the family walked, so that the load would be lighter to pull.

Climbing the mountains took all of their strength. Once Jonathan said, "My legs are so tired they don't seem to belong to me."

When their legs ached, they rested. When they were hungry, they ate. If they needed fresh meat, the two men shot squirrels and rabbits, which made delicious stews. Nothing went wrong that they couldn't fix, and everybody was cheerful most of the time.

Going down the mountains was easier. And then came the day when those weary pioneers were over the last hill. Below them lay a broad river, flowing westward.

"Hurrah! It's the Ohio," the boys shouted.

A village of forty or fifty log cabins, a few stone houses, and some stores lay on the riverbank. Flatboats glided over the muddy water, as boatmen pulled heavily on long oars with wide, sweeping strokes.

At the village Mr. Matthews sold the wagon and horses and bought a flatboat, that had a cabin where the family could eat and sleep.

There was room on the boat for a pair of oxen which he had taken as part of the price of the wagon and four horses. Then the men loaded a cow and a few pigs, chickens, and sheep that they had bought.

The family rested in the village for a few days. They bought food for the last part of their journey and listened to talk of rich soil farther west and of good places to settle.

## On the Flatboat

"Our business is finished," announced Mr. Burd one day. "Let's see what lies ahead." The two men pushed the boat off with long poles and sent it floating down the stream.

"Traveling by flatboat is fun," Sally decided that very first day. It was, indeed!

The boat made no noise, and at dusk they saw deer that came to the river to drink. Fishing was fun, too. Using salt pork for bait, they caught all the fish they could eat. For days they floated along between hilly banks lined with bushes and tangled vines that grew down to the water's edge.

Sometimes they saw canoes and other boats floating down the swiftly flowing stream. Day after day the boat glided along, going about six miles an hour. The men watched carefully to steer the flatboat away from logs and trees that were half-hidden below the surface of the water.

At night they tied the boat in a sheltered spot, and continued their journey in daylight. At some places they tied up the boat for several days. So it was about thirty days before the pioneers came to the place where they had decided to settle.

A mile or two ahead smoke was curling from the chimneys of a few log huts scattered along the riverbank.

"That must be Trader's Point," said Mr. Matthews. "There's the point of land that we've been told about. Let's go ashore and see if the soil is as good as folks have said." So they all clambered off the boat.

"This soil will grow good crops," said Mr. Burd as he examined a shovelful of earth. "This is the place for us."

Next day they took the boat on down the river to the village and bought one hundred acres of land. It was cheap at the price of one dollar and twenty-five cents an acre.

"We'll start clearing the land tomorrow," Mr. Burd declared. "Then we must plant a garden and fence in a place for the animals."

"Where can we live until our new house is built?" asked Sally.

"Right here on the boat, of course," said her father. "It will be a long time before a house is finished, because we first must clear several acres of land and get a crop of corn planted."

# A New Home at Last

Clearing the land was a hard task. Day after day the men worked, pulling up tangled vines and bushes and cutting down trees. They rolled the logs to a place near a spring where the new house was to stand.

In the meantime Mother and the children planted the rose and lilac bushes. Sally and Jonathan collected stones for a chimney, while Andy made rough shingles for the roof.

It was past the middle of summer before the men had time to finish the log walls and nail on the shingles. Then Father said, "Tomorrow we'll tear up the flatboat and use the lumber to make a floor."

It didn't take long to lay the floor and to finish the windows and doors. They used the lumber that was left over to make their beds, tables, and chairs. Next they stretched greased paper over the windows to take the place of glass, and their pioneer home was ready at last.

One day soon after they were settled in their new home, a man in a canoe hailed them from the river. He told about the arrival of soldiers at the log fort in Trader's Point.

"Come tomorrow and help us celebrate," he called out. "Folks from miles around will be there."

So very early the next morning the Burds walked to town with Mr. Matthews. They were just in time to see a grand sight.

The United States flag was being raised at the fort for the first time. Soon the bright colors were waving in the breeze— a star and a stripe for each state.

"Thirteen stars and thirteen stripes," said Jonathan, looking up. "I like that flag."

"Yes," said Father, "it's a good flag, and it's a good country. I'm glad we're here."

# The Neighborhood Needle

In a year's time a few more families had come westward to settle near Trader's Point. A few more scattered farms had been cut out of the thick forest, and new log cabins stood among the stumps of the cleared acres near the Ohio.

All the work on these pioneer farms was done by hand, and each member of a family had to do his share. Boys helped their fathers, and girls learned to cook, spin, and mend, and to do housework of all kinds.

Among these new pioneers was the Sparks family. Mary Sparks was only eight, but she was learning to darn so that she could help her mother do the mending for the family. Before Mary was allowed to darn socks, she practiced on old dishtowels, learning to fill the holes evenly and firmly.

Needles were scarce, and when a family lost or broke the ones they had, they would borrow from another family. It happened that Mrs. Sparks owned the only darning needle in the whole neighborhood. But she was always glad to lend it to anyone.

Every time Mary used it, she would put the needle carefully away in the sewing basket. But on the day that she was to darn her father's socks for the first time, the needle wasn't in its usual place.

"Oh, now I remember!" said Mrs. Sparks. "I let Mrs. Burd have the darning needle last week, and she hasn't returned it. Mary, you must go and tell her that we'll want the needle today. Then she may borrow it again."

Mary put on her calico sunbonnet, tied a clean apron around her waist, and started her mile-and-a-half walk. She skipped along the shady trail, singing all the way.

Mrs. Burd and Sally gladly welcomed Mary's arrival, and Mrs. Burd brought out the needle at once. Before she gave it to Mary, she pushed it through a scrap of cloth for safekeeping.

"Put it in your apron pocket, child," said Mrs. Burd. "Then you'll not risk losing it. Tell your mother I'm thankful she could lend me the needle. It's a shame you had to come for it, but I'm glad the errand gave you an excuse to visit us. Here's a cookie to eat on the way home."

"Oh, thank you," said Mary. "I'm always glad to come to your house."

On the way back Mary kept feeling in her pocket to be sure that the needle was still there. But she forgot it when she stopped and gathered some wood lilies. Humming a gay song, she laid her lilies on a log and began picking a bunch of purple flowers.

Before starting on, she felt once more in her pocket. The cloth was there, but the darning needle was gone! It had slipped through the scrap of cloth and had pushed on through her apron pocket.

Mary's heart beat fast. The needle must be found! It was too precious to lose. She knelt at one end of the big oak log and crept along on her hands and knees, searching anxiously for the long thin needle.

At the end of the log Mary straightened up, and her eyes opened wide in fright.

There, facing her, was an Indian girl about thirteen years old. Just back of the girl stood an Indian man, with a blanket drawn around his shoulders. Mary closed her lips tightly to choke back a cry of alarm.

"How!" said the Indian man.

Mary knew that was an Indian greeting.

"How!" she answered in a trembling voice.

Then the Indian smiled, and Mary's fear left her. The man pointed toward the place where she had been searching and spoke questioningly in the Indian language.

The words were strange to Mary, but she guessed that he was asking why she had been creeping along, patting the leaves.

Mary couldn't speak the Indian language, but she tried to act out what had happened. First she pretended to be sewing her apron. Next she acted as if she were placing the needle in her pocket. Then she turned her pocket wrong-side out and pointed to the ground, showing that a needle had been lost.

To Mary's astonishment, both Indians knelt down and began to search also. All three went crawling about, examining the ground.

Soon there was a soft grunt from the man as he held up the precious needle, and Mary reached for it with a cry of joy.

"Thank you!" she cried, wondering what she could do in return. Then she noticed a three-cornered tear in the man's blanket. She tugged at it gently until he took it off.

Sitting down, she spread the torn part of the blanket over her knee.

Mary drew a woolen thread from one edge of the blanket. Then she threaded the needle and began to darn the tear, weaving the edges together carefully.

When it was mended, the man hung the blanket over his shoulder again and said a single word in the Indian language. By the pleased look in his eyes, Mary knew that he meant to thank her.

The two Indians took the path back into the forest, and Mary went on home, clutching the thin needle in her hand all the way.

After she had put her flowers in water, she sat down to darn Father's socks. She was careful to weave the yarn over and under and fill the holes smoothly. All the while her tongue was as busy as her fingers, telling of her adventure with the Indians.

"You were a good girl to mend the man's blanket," her mother told her in approval.

Father came in, and he praised Mary for mending his socks so well. "They're almost like new," he said as he examined them. When he heard about the Indians, he praised her again for being kind and thoughtful.

Two days later Mary's father took her to the village where the Indians lived. When she saw the two Indians whom she had met in the woods, Mary smiled, and they smiled back. Then the man proudly let Mr. Sparks examine the neat bit of mending that Mary had done on his blanket.

Next day as she sat on a bench by the door cutting pieces for a quilt, the two Indians suddenly appeared in the yard. They held out two gifts for Mary. One gift was a pair of deerskin moccasins, with porcupine quills sewed on them for trimming. The other was a grass basket.

"What lovely gifts!" cried Mary, throwing her arms around the girl and hugging her.

After that the Indian maid and the pioneer girl became well acquainted, and soon they knew enough of each other's language to have good times together.

Mary wore the moccasins every day. The basket was just the right size for her sewing, and it was the best place of all to keep the neighborhood needle.

# Hasty Pudding

### Betty in Charge

Thirty miles from Trader's Point was the lonely hillside farm of the Barker family. One March day the three children were to stay at home while their parents made the long journey up the valley road to town.

They were to be gone two days, and ten-year-old Betty was to be in charge of the house. She had to see that all went well until the arrival of Uncle John and Aunt Hulda, who would stay all night.

Mr. Barker was taking wheat and corn to the mill to be ground into flour and meal. In his wagon were potatoes, ham, and bacon, to be traded at the store for other things that were needed—salt, sugar, a new hoe, a pail of molasses, and ten yards of calico.

"Now remember, Betty," said her mother, "the family is depending on you. Don't forget what I've told you."

"I'll not forget a single thing," Betty said, "and I'm going to make hasty pudding for supper. I've watched you make it, and I'm sure I know how."

With her last good-bys, Mrs. Barker gave two more directions. "Be sure to keep the fire going. Be sure to bar the door when it begins to get dark."

Then Mr. and Mrs. Barker climbed into the wagon, clucked to the horses, and were off.

The children watched until they were past the big curve in the valley road. It was just sun-up, but Betty could not help wishing that it were evening and that Aunt Hulda and Uncle John were already there.

The forenoon passed quickly, for all three children were busy. After the noon meal they sat around the fire to rest. Tom and Martha fell asleep, and Betty spent more time looking at a book than she should have.

Suddenly she jumped up and stared at the clock in surprise. She had let the best part of the afternoon go by without making the pudding. Now she must do the milking before she could start supper.

All three children went out at once to do their chores. Tom carried grain and water to the oxen and other animals. Martha's task was to scatter corn for the chickens, and Betty milked the cow. She brought in the milk and began to mix the pudding, humming happily as she worked.

Carefully she measured and poured milk into the iron pot hanging in the fireplace. Then she measured corn meal and stirred it into the boiling milk until it was a thick porridge. Last of all she added crumbs of maple sugar to give a delicious taste to the pudding. But minutes slipped quickly by, and suppertime came long before she was ready.

Martha and Tom came in tired and hungry. Tom grumbled because supper wasn't ready, and Martha was about to burst into tears. To cheer her, Betty said quickly, "I'll have supper ready before you know it. Try to be patient a little longer."

At last the bacon was a golden brown, and so were the crusty skins of the potatoes, greased with bacon fat and baked on the hearth.

"Get plates and bowls and spoons, Martha," said Betty as she lifted the pot from the hook and took off the lid.

## An Unexpected Guest

All at once there was a faint scratching and fumbling at the door. At that instant Betty remembered her mother's order to bar the door as soon as it began to get dark.

Betty stood stiff with fear, her eyes on the door. Suddenly the wooden latch lifted, and the door swung open.

The firelight shone on two small, glowing eyes and a huge, furry body. There in the doorway stood a big black bear!

Hastily Betty set the pot on the hearth and shouted, "Martha, Tom! Run up the ladder to the loft!"

In a moment all three were sitting on the edge of the loft with their feet hanging down. Then a sudden breeze, blowing through the house, banged the door shut. The bar of the latch slipped down, and the door was fastened tight.

The bear waddled over to the table, rose on his hind feet, and scooped up the bacon. Next he gobbled up the potatoes, and then he caught the scent of the hasty pudding.

Shuffling over to the hearth, he plunged his nose into the pot. That pudding was hot, and it burned him. He backed away, sat down on the floor, and rocked from side to side, holding his paw to his nose.

This comical sight was too much for the children, and they giggled. The bear looked up, and for a full minute he stared at his audience. Then in a stiff, shuffling walk he came across the room and awkwardly began climbing the ladder.

Up he clambered, step by step.

Betty knew she must think of something to do before he came nearer. Her brother and sister were depending on her.

"Tom," she whispered, motioning toward the ladder, "take hold of the other side and help me shove."

By pushing with all their strength, they shoved the ladder away. Down it went with a clatter to the floor below, knocking a jar of molasses off a shelf as it fell.

The bear tumbled lightly, like a huge cat, curling himself into a ball and rolling over and over, unharmed. The children laughed loud and long at the comical sight.

The bear paid no attention to them after he found that he could not get up to where they were. He licked up the molasses. He upset a sewing basket, tangling the thread and balls of yarn. Then he walked around, poking his nose into everything.

Suddenly he seemed to be displeased over not finding any more food, for he plunged against the table and upset it, with a great clatter.

The house looked as though a windstorm had blown through it. But no matter what the bear did, he looked so comical that the children could not stop their laughter. In spite of all the mischief he was doing, they could not be angry at a creature who was only looking for food.

Betty finally noticed how dark the loft was getting. Night had already begun.

"Uncle John and Aunt Hulda certainly will be here soon," she said to Tom.

Each of them, in that second, was thinking of the same thing, although it was Tom who mentioned it first.

"Uncle John always carries his gun everywhere he goes. When he sees the bear, he will shoot it."

"Oh, no, he can't!" wailed Martha. "He mustn't! He shan't kill our bear."

The bear had begun to seem like a playmate who had entertained them through an exciting hour. They actually forgot that he had gobbled up their supper and kept them trapped in the loft for an hour. Their one thought was how to save the bear's life when their uncle came with his gun.

## Tom to the Rescue

"If the bear could just get outside," Betty said helplessly. "But all the windows are too small, and the door is latched."

As Betty mentioned the latched door, Tom thought of a way to solve their problem.

He fumbled in his pocket and drew out a long piece of cord. At the end of it he tied a long loop.

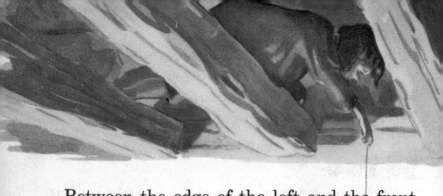

Between the edge of the loft and the front wall of the house were big wooden beams. One beam was just above the door, and at the risk of falling, Tom got over to it.

Stretching out full-length, he lowered the cord, letting it slide along the door.

"Are you going to catch the bear with that string?" teased Martha.

Tom just shook his head and kept his eyes on the loop as it came near the latch on the door beneath him.

Tom intended to hook the loop under the latch. Once he tried and failed. Then he attempted it again.

The motion of the cord caught the bear's attention, and he walked over to sniff it.

Tom held his breath. If the bear should snatch the cord and break it, Tom's plan to save that mischievous animal from his uncle's gun would fail.

Tom hadn't much time, for his aunt and uncle might come any minute now.

But his third attempt was successful, and the loop caught. Tom jerked the cord quickly and lifted the latch. Slowly the door swung open, and the bear went shuffling out with a grunt, disappearing in the darkness.

As soon as the amusing visitor had gone, Tom swung himself down from the beam and dropped to the floor beneath. He closed the door and barred it and put the ladder up for the girls.

Just as they were scrambling down, they heard their aunt and uncle calling outside. As Tom opened the door, the two grown-ups stared past their nephew into the wrecked room, that looked like a bad dream.

Uncle John whistled in astonishment, and his wife gasped, "My goodness! Who did all this mischief?"

"Just a big bear!" giggled Betty. "But, oh, Aunt Hulda! I made hasty pudding! It was a wonderful one! Only I was too hasty while making it and didn't remember to bar the door. That's how the bear got in."

# Susanna Jane's Secret

One of the most exciting days ever known in Trader's Point had arrived. A school was opening! A log schoolhouse had been built—the first schoolhouse in that whole community. The schoolmaster had come to teach, and today the lessons would begin.

Susanna Jane stood on her doorstep, looking toward the log schoolhouse near the fort. Her lips trembled with disappointment, and tears had begun to sting her eyes.

Her brother Abel was going to school, but Susanna Jane was not allowed to go because she was a girl.

"Oh, Mother!" she cried. "What difference does it make whether I am a girl or not? Why can't girls go to school?"

Mrs. Hand put her arm about her daughter's waist, saying, "Some girls do go to school, I believe. But girls have no actual need for book learning. All they need to learn are things like spinning, sewing, weaving, knitting, cooking, and soap making."

"But that isn't fair!" argued Susanna.

"What isn't fair, daughter?" said a voice. Turning her head quickly, Susanna Jane caught sight of her father in the doorway.

"About—th-the—school," she stammered, fumbling at her collar. "Let me go. Please!"

Mr. Hand shook his head. "No, Susanna. I'd let you go if you needed book learning. But it's not necessary. Girls don't need it."

"M-m-maybe you're right," Susanna Jane murmured in disappointment. And then a daring and determined plan flashed into her mind. If only it would be successful!

"Oh, Father!" she exclaimed. "Will the new schoolmaster board with us?"

"Yes, I reckon so," her father answered. "He'll take turns staying with each family. His board is part of his pay for teaching."

That afternoon, when it was time for school to be over, Susanna Jane left the cabin and sped through the forest toward the school. The woods path was much longer, but she kept away from the clearing because she did not want to risk meeting Abel. He must not know what she intended to do.

At last she reached the school. Through the open door she saw the vacant room. The pupils were gone, of course, but what if the teacher had left, too? Susanna's heart beat rapidly. Her throat felt dry.

She crept closer and looked in. She could see the teacher's desk and the long benches of rough boards. A large fireplace filled one wall, and in the corner was a pail of water and a long-handled dipper.

Suddenly there was a step on the path, and Susanna Jane turned to find herself facing a tall young man with a serious, boyish face.

"Good afternoon," he said, pleasantly.

"Oh—I—I was looking for the schoolmaster," stammered Susanna Jane.

"I am the schoolmaster," he said, smiling. "My name is Duncan Gates."

Susanna stared in astonishment. Why, he looked no more than eighteen. How could a teacher be so young?

Suddenly she burst out, "I want to study at school, and Father won't let me, because he says a girl doesn't need book learning. I thought that maybe—when you come to board with us—you'd try to teach me. If you will, I'll do all your mending and clean your writing pens and your boots."

The young man looked at her kindly.

"What is your name?" he asked.

"Susanna Jane Hand, sir. Will you please teach me? I'm depending on it so much."

"Of course!" Duncan Gates answered, patting her head. "Your lessons will start in two weeks, when I come to board with you."

"Thank you so much!" cried Susanna. "I must go now," she added hastily. "Please don't mention this to anyone."

"I promise," laughed Duncan Gates. Then the happy girl ran up the path, her deerskin moccasins twinkling in the fallen leaves.

At supper that night she said to her father coaxingly, "When the schoolmaster comes here, could I study with him—just a little?"

Mr. Hand slowly thought the matter over. Then he coughed and said, "I reckon we'll let you try it, if the master is willing."

Susanna finished her supper contentedly. She knew the schoolmaster would be willing. But that was her secret.

Two weeks passed, and the time came for Duncan Gates to board at Susanna's house. He gave her a lesson the first evening and almost every night of his stay. Even after he had gone to board with another family, he continued her lessons. Susanna studied hard and learned rapidly.

But one frosty night after harvest there wasn't any lesson, for old Zeke Benson had invited the whole community to a party.

The party was a Husking Bee, and all the guests gathered in Zeke's barn. Piles of cornstalks, with unhusked ears, were stacked on the floor, and fat candles were fastened up for light. All the folks for miles around came to husk the corn, and everyone had fun.

Zeke played his old brown fiddle, while jokes, laughter, and cheery shouts filled the barn to the very shingles on the roof. Work seemed to fly as fast as friendly tongues could wag.

Bushels of corn were husked and the stalks stored away for fodder. Then the women unpacked huge baskets of food.

After the workers ate and rested, Duncan Gates said, "Folks, I suggest a Spelldown!"

The people clapped their hands eagerly. Spelldowns were fun and gave a chance to examine the pupils. The boys lined up just a little anxiously, with a clatter of big awkward boots. The young master stood before them, ready to pronounce the words from a book in his hands.

"You come, too, Susanna Jane!" he said.

Everyone looked amazed—even Susanna's parents. But she walked proudly to the head of the line, her plump cheeks as pink as her brand-new calico dress.

"Necessary," pronounced the master, and nodded as Susanna spelled the word correctly.

"Elbow," pronounced the master, looking at Abraham Sparks, who was next in line.

"E-l-b-o," he spelled. It was wrong, and poor Abraham sat down, looking just a bit shamefaced at missing the word.

*Dipper* was the next word pronounced. Bartholomew Swift spelled it correctly. But Andy Burd missed the word *measure* by leaving out the *a*. So he was down, too.

Then in an astonishingly short time such words as *cough*, *calico*, *gnaw*, *mischief*, *tease*, and *moccasin* had been missed by all the spellers except Susanna Jane and Abel.

Next the master pronounced, "Canoe."

Abel took a deep breath.

"K-n-e-w," he spelled, promptly.

"Wrong," said the schoolmaster, and Abel sat down. Now Susanna Jane was standing by herself, her heart beating excitedly.

"Canoe," repeated the master.

Susanna Jane lifted her head with pride and spelled, "C-a-n-o-e."

"Correct!" declared the schoolmaster, and to everyone's astonishment, a girl had won the spelling-match!

"Susanna Jane, I'm right proud of you!" said her father, and her mother kissed and hugged her, beaming with pride.

There was a great deal of noisy praise, and then the master called for attention.

"Susanna Jane has done all her studying at home," he said. "She'd do even better if she were at school. I hope that she and all the girls can come to school. For any girl who learns as rapidly as Susanna, could teach a school of her own some day and earn at least eighteen dollars a month!"

The crowd gasped. Eighteen–dollars–a–month! They could hardly believe that any girl alive could earn that much money—just with book learning. Mr. Hand coughed and cleared his throat. "I am planning to send Susanna Jane to school after this," he said.

"I want Mary to go, too," said Mr. Sparks.

Then a hum of happy, excited voices filled the air as other parents made arrangements for their girls to go to school.

Susanna Jane's heart gave a joyful leap. She and other girls like her were actually going to have book learning, too!

# A Boy and His Book

As the years went by, more and more people came into the great Ohio River valley. In wagons, in flatboats, on horseback, and on foot those pioneers struggled bravely to gain new homes in the West.

Many went far beyond Trader's Point, pushing steadily westward. New farms were chopped out of the forests. New log cabins and towns were built, and if a teacher came to a community, a school was started.

In a lonely log cabin near Pigeon Creek lived a boy called Abe who wanted to get book learning more than anything else. When he heard of a new school nine miles away, Abe told his sister Sally, and they got ready to walk the whole distance.

Nancy, their mother, saw that they were neat and clean and sent them off with a loving pat.

"Now go and learn all you can," she said.
And away they went, hand in hand, dressed in
clothing made entirely by their mother. She
had even made Abe's cap from the skin of a
raccoon and his boots from bearskin.

After the first few days Sally tired of
the long eighteen-mile walk and didn't go
any more. But to young Abe, no distance
seemed too great if only he could learn to
write and spell and to read what was written
in books.

Less than a month later, the school closed
so that the pupils could help with the spring
planting. Abe was disappointed, but he knew
that the farmers needed all the help they
could get to raise and harvest their crops.
So he helped with the work uncomplainingly.

Abe was big and strong for a boy who was not yet thirteen, and he did a man's work. But no matter what he was doing, he never stopped thinking about books and wishing he knew what was in them.

The next year a strange illness brought sorrow to the community at Pigeon Creek. It was an illness so terrible that many people died, and Abe's mother was one of them.

For a long time afterward Abe didn't go to school. He spent his time helping Sally with the housework or hunting and fishing. Then one day his father brought home a new wife, with three children of her own.

The new wife was a good mother to Abe and Sally. She knew how much Abe wanted book learning and sent him back to school. But school was open for only a few weeks during the winter, and often Abe had to stay at home and help his father chop wood and do other chores.

In those few weeks of schooling the boy learned to read, write, spell, and figure. But what he liked best of all was reading.

Books were scarce in Abe's neighborhood. His family owned only two—a Bible and an old arithmetic. The Bible he read as best he could, often stumbling over the words he couldn't pronounce. And the arithmetic he studied from cover to cover. He borrowed every book anyone could lend him and read each one until he almost knew it by heart.

One cold day he walked five miles to help a farmer pull cornstalks for fodder. When he came to dinner at noon, he saw a book on a table and asked if he might borrow it. Abe's eyes sparkled with joy when he left with the book tucked under his arm.

That night he stretched out flat on the dirt floor before the crackling fire with his book. He read until midnight by the light of the glowing flames.

When he went to his bed in the loft, Abe tucked the book between two logs. Next morning, when he reached out for it, his fingers touched something cold and wet.

The precious book was soaked with snow that had blown in through the cracks. It was ruined, and the only honest thing to do was to go and tell the owner. This he did promptly, without waiting for breakfast.

"Please, sir," said Abe, when he had told the farmer his sorrowful story, "I'll pull fodder or do anything you say to make up for ruining your book."

"Well," said the farmer, "I reckon about two days' work will pay for it. Pull fodder for two days, and you can keep the book."

So Abe worked for two days, not caring if his back ached and his hands were stiff with cold. The book was actually his!

Years afterward, when young Abe Lincoln grew up and was President Abraham Lincoln, he often said that this book had helped his dreams come true. It was the story of the life of George Washington, who was the first President of the United States of America.

# Wool Gathering

Christmas was drawing near. But it was bringing worry to Sarah Ann White as she sat by the crackling fire in a new log cabin near Pigeon Creek. Her worry was what to give her father for Christmas.

She already had a present for her mother. When they had left their home in the East, Aunt Polly had given her several pretty handkerchiefs. One was of white linen, with a fancy edge—just the thing for Mother.

But what about her father? She couldn't buy him a gift, because the town was so far away that the family made trips there only when it was necessary. And, besides, she had no money and nothing to trade, even if she could get to town.

The spruce logs were burning brightly, but all their snapping and crackling could not cheer Sarah Ann.

Her mother was sitting on a bench by the greased paper window, bent close over her darning. "Socks are what Father needs," she said. "These are nothing but holes."

"Oh," cried Sarah Ann, "I'll knit a pair of socks for Father's present."

"But there's not enough yarn to make two socks," said Sarah's mother. "Yarn is now getting to be as scarce as hens' teeth."

Mother was always saying that something was "as scarce as hens' teeth," and Sarah knew what she meant. A hen had no teeth at all! So how could Sarah knit socks for Father if she hadn't the yarn?

"Why can't we spin the yarn?" Sarah asked, looking at her mother's spinning wheel.

"We haven't any wool," replied her mother. "I've used all the wool that we sheared from our flock of sheep before we left the East."

"Could we shear my pet lamb and get some more wool?" Sarah Ann asked hopefully.

"Gracious, no!" exclaimed Mother. "If we shear her in wintertime, she will freeze."

All that morning Sarah Ann kept wondering how she could get some wool for a pair of socks.

Shortly after noon the sun came out. It made Sarah Ann want to go outdoors.

"May I go to see Lucy Carter?" she asked when she had finished washing the dishes.

Mother nodded her head and said, "If you start home by three-thirty. Remember that darkness comes early these winter days."

As soon as she reached the cabin where her friend Lucy lived, Sarah Ann began to talk about her need for wool.

"Well," said Lucy's mother, "Mr. Mills has a flock of sheep. He probably has wool left from shearing time and would sell some."

"But I've no money," replied Sarah Ann.

"I saw the sheep yesterday," said Lucy. "Mr. Mills was driving them east along the river path through all the thorn bushes."

"Thorns!" cried Sarah Ann, her black eyes snapping. She hastily put on her shawl and hood. "Let's go down there now!"

"Must we?" asked Lucy in dismay. "I had planned to knit a jacket for my doll."

But Sarah was already speeding toward the river path. Lucy followed her, putting on her shawl and hood as she ran.

"See?" Sarah Ann cried, reaching into the thorn bushes. "There are tufts of wool on these thorns! I'm glad Mr. Mills drove his sheep along this river path!"

Her swift fingers began gathering woolly tufts that were clinging to the bushes.

"I'll go home and get a sack," Lucy offered.

"Oh, fine!" said Sarah Ann, scrambling into a bush after an extra large tuft. She had a lapful of wool when Lucy returned.

For two whole hours the girls worked. At last Lucy looked up at the dark sky. "It must be going to snow," she announced. "Look at those black clouds."

"Gracious!" exclaimed Sarah, clutching her shawl tightly. "We must go, or we'll get soaking wet. Good-by, Lucy!"

Mother was anxiously watching for Sarah.

"Where have you been so long, child?" she asked. "I was uneasy! And what are you carrying in that big sack?"

"Wool!" cried Sarah with pride. "A big sack of it, and it didn't cost me a penny! The sheep rubbed it off on the thorn bushes. Let's keep this a secret and give Father new socks for Christmas."

"Oh, yes!" said Mother. "It's lucky that he's working away from home. He can't possibly discover our secret."

After that they were very busy, washing the wool and drying it. As the two worked together, spinning and winding the yarn, Sarah sang a Christmas song to the merry hum of the wheel.

Mother soaked the yarn in a dye pot, and out it came, a lovely blue. But after the yarn was dyed, Sarah had another worry. She had trouble keeping the yarn on the four thin needles.

"You'd better let me knit the socks for you," said her mother. "You may ruin them."

"Oh, no!" came Sarah's prompt reply. "I want to make Father's socks myself."

She kept trying, and before long she was knitting quite smoothly and amazingly fast.

Mother had a secret she was keeping from Sarah. One day she went to Mrs. Carter's with some sewing hidden under her shawl, while Sarah knitted contentedly at home.

Finally it was the night before Christmas. Father had come home, and the cabin was gay with evergreens and red winterberries from the woods.

Sarah had already tucked her presents in the stockings by the chimney when Mother said, "Now, Sarah Ann, you go up to bed. Father and I want to play Santa Claus."

So Sarah climbed up to her bed in the loft. How could she wait until morning?

When dawn came, Sarah Ann scrambled down the ladder. There, pinned to her stocking, was a new dress her mother had made. Inside the stocking was a pair of leather moccasins from Father.

Mother was delighted with her present from Sarah and a handkerchief box from Father. He admired a deerskin jacket that Mother had made and the lovely warm blue socks. When he heard how Sarah had made the socks, he could not hug her close enough.

Laying his cheek against Sarah's, he said, "Our first Christmas in our log house is a happy one."

"That makes it our home," cried Mother. "For no house is really home until you've had a happy Christmas in it."

# Steam Comes Upriver

### Exciting News

As time went on, the folks along the river began to hear about a new kind of boat. It had a wood-burning engine that puffed smoke from a tall smokestack and turned a paddle wheel to make the boat go. Everybody was anxious to see this new steamboat. But no one waited more anxiously than Amos Mills, who stood on the riverbank at dawn on one cold Saturday in March.

Amos should have been doing the chores, because his father was away helping a cousin split wood for fences. But instead of going straight to milk the cow, Amos had gone to the river to look for the boat.

As he stood there trying to imagine how the boat would look as it steamed around the bend, his thoughts were interrupted by the sound of galloping hoofs.

"Steamboat's coming today!" the rider said. "I'm riding ahead to ask the farmers to have wood for the boat stacked along the riverbank. Captain Green will pay a good price for firewood. He will shoot off the cannon on deck as a signal when he reaches the bend in the river. That will give folks time to get down to the shore."

The rider wheeled and galloped off, while Amos almost stumbled over his milk pail as he hurried to milk the cow.

Of course he intended to sell the Captain their extra fuel, just as Father would if he were home. They had several sled loads of firewood in the wood lot half a mile away. All winter long Amos had worked there during his spare time, splitting wood. He would haul some of this wood to the riverbank.

That was what he could do to help the new steamboat. It would help the family, too, for money was scarce, and whatever the Captain might offer would be very welcome.

Amos did the milking quickly and rushed to tell his mother and sister about his plan to sell wood for the new steamboat. Then he ran back to finish his chores and to harness old Dan to the sled.

At the cabin door he met Abbie, dressed in a warm deerskin coat and a raccoon cap that matched his own.

"I'm going along," she said, hurrying to jump on the sled. "Mother says I may help you load."

The way to the wood lot was scarcely more than a rough, bumpy trail. But old Dan was used to such traveling and picked his way carefully between the stumps.

On reaching the woodpiles, Amos hopped off and commenced loading. Abbie tugged and lifted, too, but the task took longer than they had expected. When finally they had heaped on as much as Dan could haul, they turned toward the river.

Amos and Abbie unloaded the wood on the bank and went back for more. Several times they stopped old Dan to listen for the boat, but there was only the silence of the forest.

They viewed their second load with proud approval and thought of the extra money it would bring for the family pocketbook.

"Giddap! Giddap!" they shouted.

Dan started, and the two children walked beside him, guiding him by the reins.

As the faint chug of an engine broke the silence, they realized that the big steamboat was nearing the bend. Suddenly the roar of a cannon burst on the air. Snorting with fear, Dan plunged, and commenced to run. The loaded sled went bumpety, bump against the stumps as Amos attempted to halt him.

"Whoa!" yelled Amos at the snorting horse.

Suddenly Dan stumbled. His left hind foot had caught in a heap of snow-covered stones, and he came to a trembling standstill.

Abbie stood at his head and spoke gently to him, while Amos worked for a long time trying to free Dan's foot. When finally he got it loose, he discovered that Dan had skinned a patch of hide from his leg and a sharp stone was stuck firmly in his hoof. Amos could not loosen it.

"What can we do?" the boy wondered.

The Captain was depending on their wood, and if they left Dan and ran to see the boat, how would they get the fuel to him?

"Run, Abbie," said Amos, "and ask Mother to harness the ox. We'll hobble along and meet you, and then I'll hitch the ox to the sled in place of Dan."

Abbie ran. She had never run faster.

The steamboat's engine pounded loudly now, but the sounds soon grew less and less clear. And when Abbie came in sight of the river, there was only a plume of feathery gray smoke drifting over the water. The steamboat had vanished entirely from sight, and Abbie's mother was returning from the riverbank. "Oh, has the steamboat gone?" gasped Abbie in dismay.

Mother nodded. "Why didn't you children jump on Dan and come down to see it?"

"Oh, we couldn't," wailed Abbie. "Old Dan took fright at the cannon and tried to run away. He picked up a stone in his foot, and so he's lame. He can barely hobble."

The idea of old Dan trying to run away was comical to Mother. "Oh, oh," she laughed. "Nothing except a cannon would ever make old Dan run! But you and Amos needn't feel so bad, for Captain Green took your pile of wood and paid me for it. He'll stop on his return trip Tuesday to get some more fuel. You'll see the steamboat then." And with that promise, the children had to be content.

### A Happy Surprise

Early Tuesday morning Amos and Abbie were leading Dan to the river to soak his lame foot. Suddenly Abbie cried, "The boat's coming! There's smoke beyond the trees!"

Soon afterward they heard the steam engine rumbling and the big paddle wheel churning. Then the big boat drew into view, splashing and chugging. Amos could not tear his eyes away from it. The folks who had gathered there cheered as it glided to the bank.

Captain Green hailed Amos and said, "Well, young fellow! Got any wood for us?"

Amos nodded, motioning toward the wood that he and Abbie had hauled with the ox.

The Captain came ashore and measured the stack of wood. As he counted out the price, he said, "You didn't get here Saturday. So come aboard while the fuel is being loaded."

Timidly, but full of excitement, the two children walked up the plank that led to the deck of that grand steamboat.

Captain Green himself showed them all about. They saw the black cannon on deck. They went below and saw the steam engine that ran the boat. They saw the furs and other goods that the Captain was taking to the river towns to sell or trade.

They came up on deck again and went into a vacant cabin to see where passengers slept. They were amazed at the shelves that let down from the walls for beds.

Last of all the Captain led them proudly to the pilot house to see the great wheel that steered the boat.

As the children walked down the plank, Captain Green said, "Stay aboard and ride down to Fort Washington with us."

Amos's gray eyes got very big, and Abbie's mouth went into a big round O. Then Amos swallowed hopelessly and shook his head.

"I—can't go and leave old Dan," he said. Then he explained about the lame foot.

"Ha!" said the Captain. "There's a good horse doctor at Fort Washington. We can leave Dan with the doctor, and you children can stay on the steamboat. We'll pick up the horse on our return trip Friday. Since my cannon caused old Dan to get hurt, I'd better do my part in helping him get well."

"Thank you, sir," said Amos, "but I have to stay here and do the chores while Father is away."

"I'll do all your chores," interrupted a neighbor's voice. "You and Abbie go along."

"Yes," nodded their mother. "Take Dan and get the doctor to fix his lame foot."

So they led the hobbling horse aboard, and Amos couldn't help thinking that steam was a fine thing for everybody, even for Dan!

# Wonders
of Our Times

# Radio Rescue

The first of October was moving day for the King family. Tables, chairs, and beds were set out in the front yard. A moving van had come into the driveway, and the movers were loading it with furniture and boxes as fast as they could.

Mr. and Mrs. King were busy giving all the necessary directions to the men. Kitty and Don hustled back and forth, carrying bundles to put into the car. Even little Ann worked hard, keeping out of their way and at the same time trying to see everything.

Pal, the dog, whined in a puzzled tone as each object disappeared into the van. At last the van was filled, and the children watched in silence as it started off to the new house on the other side of the city.

"Well," said Father, "we may as well go, too. The sooner we get to our new house, the sooner we'll feel at home there."

They were moving just a few miles away, but all the unfamiliar streets made Kitty and Don feel as if they were in an entirely different city. Even Pal seemed to be uneasy.

But when the family reached the new house and saw their furniture and pictures being unloaded, they felt more cheerful.

"There's my bed," cried Kitty.

"There's mine," echoed Ann.

"Here's the radio!" Don exclaimed.

They rushed from one piece of furniture to another, hailing each familiar object as if it were an old friend. Pal bounded after them, barking excitedly. Don turned on the radio the minute it was in place, and as the movers arranged the rest of the furniture, the house began to seem homelike.

Finally the moving van drove away. Then Father went back to his work at the factory, and Mother hustled off to the grocery store.

"Take care of Ann," she called to Don and Kitty. "Unpack your toys and put them on the shelves in the attic playroom."

The children eagerly commenced poking about in search of their special treasures.

"I want my rag doll," mumbled Ann as she followed Kitty to the attic. "I left my doll under the lilac bush, and I want her right now."

"Oh, forget your rag doll," Kitty urged, scarcely listening to her little sister's words. "Be a good girl and don't bother me."

"I *am* a good girl," Ann insisted. "But I want my rag doll, and I'm going to get her."

Still mumbling to herself, Ann wandered down the stairs and out to the front porch. Then with a determined look on her small, round face, she started up the street in the bright October sunshine.

Nearly an hour later Mrs. King returned from buying her groceries and came up to the attic in search of the children.

"Where's Ann?" she asked as she looked about the playroom.

"She's here somewhere," Don answered, hunting for some glue to mend his model airplane. "Here, Pal! Find Ann!"

Pal bounded off, sniffing and snuffing along the bare planks of the attic floor.

"Ann *was* right here," Kitty said, feeling guilty because she had forgotten her sister. But Ann *wasn't* right there. She wasn't downstairs or in the basement or in the yard.

"Look in the cupboards," suggested Kitty, feeling more guilty every minute.

"Oh, Ann, Ann!" called Mother anxiously. "Don't be naughty. Stop trying to fool us." But no happy giggle answered her command. Ann was not hiding. She had vanished.

"I'll telephone Father at the factory and call the police," Mrs. King decided with a sinking heart. "Don, run to the neighbors and ask if they have seen a little girl with yellow braids and a pink dress."

Just then there came a sudden barking and whining from the living room.

"Pal has found Ann!" shouted Don.

But when they reached the living room, there was no sign of Ann. Pal stood before the radio, snuffing at the loud-speaker and whining frantically.

"Oh-h," Kitty sighed in disappointment. "Pal's just barking at the radio. They must be broadcasting one of those pet programs, and he's heard a cat or another dog."

But it was neither a barking dog nor a mewing cat that Pal had recognized. For just then they all heard a childish voice saying, "My name is Ann. I left my rag doll under the lilac bush, but I can't find her. I lost my rag doll, and I lost myself, too."

"Gracious! That's Ann talking!" gasped Mrs. King in amazement. "Where is she?"

Then a man's voice interrupted. "This is the Man-on-the-Street program, broadcasting in front of the Palace Theater. You have heard a special announcement from a very young lady named Ann. She has blue eyes, yellow braids, and a pink dress. If anyone knows her, please come and get her."

The message was scarcely finished before Mrs. King had hustled Kitty and Don into the car. As they reached the theater and broke through the curious crowd, they spied Ann. She was so busy broadcasting and eating ice cream that she didn't even notice she had been found.

# Messages from the Sea

Jerry Frost lived by the sea. He lived in the little village of Sandy Cove, where the houses were white, with gray roofs, and where most of the trees were evergreens.

Jerry loved the sea and everything around it. He liked to watch the sea gulls flying over the water and the ships cutting through the waves. He even liked the fogs.

It was fun to run along the beach, too, and feel the cool, damp sand beneath his bare feet. In fact, there wasn't anything about the sea that Jerry didn't like.

Every time he looked at the sea or heard it or smelled the salty sea breeze, Jerry was determined that when he grew up he would be a sea captain like his Uncle Ben.

All through October Jerry Frost had been counting the days until the first of November. That was the day on which his Uncle Ben was coming to Sandy Cove for the first time since Jerry had been born.

Uncle Ben was no ordinary uncle. He was captain of one of the largest and fastest ships that sailed the Atlantic Ocean. It could cross the Atlantic in less than four days in fair weather.

Every morning Jerry looked at the ocean to see how rough the waves were and tried to guess the distance his uncle's ship would be able to travel that day.

Jerry thought that the first of November would never come, but at last it did, and the family went to the station to meet Uncle Ben. Although Jerry had never seen his uncle, he was sure he would recognize him by his sea captain's uniform. But the only man in uniform was the conductor.

Suddenly Mother cried, "There he is!"

Jerry stared in amazement. His mother was rushing toward a tall man, but this man wore no uniform. He had on ordinary clothes.

Jerry was so disappointed that he could not keep from saying, "I thought you wore a uniform with lots of gold braid instead of just ordinary clothes."

"So I *do*," replied his uncle with a boyish smile. "But not when I'm on shore. I'll put on my uniform tonight, though, if you'd like to see it."

When Uncle Ben appeared that evening, there was no doubt about his looking like a sea captain. His uniform was dark blue with bands of gold braid. There was gold braid on his cap, too.

"Well, Jerry, here's my uniform as you ordered," said Uncle Ben, bringing his heels together and saluting. "I'm ready to receive any other orders you have for me."

Jerry's next order was for a thrilling sea story. Nothing could have suited Uncle Ben better. For the next few days Jerry heard enough sea stories to fill a dozen books.

On the last evening of Uncle Ben's visit, they had a picnic on the beach. While looking for driftwood to build a fire, Jerry picked up a bottle that had been washed ashore.

Uncle Ben said, "An old sailor once told me about finding a letter in a bottle. It was from a shipwrecked sailor who had been on a desert island for months. By the time a ship got to the island, he was dead.

"Today a wrecked ship can broadcast a radio message before it sinks. Then nearby ships usually rescue the sailors within a few hours. Before we had radio, many a bottle carried some shipwrecked sailor's message from the sea."

"I wish you'd send me a message from the sea sometime," said Jerry.

"All right," said his uncle. "I'll send you a radiogram. I'll send it at noon on my first day at sea, and you'll receive it within a few hours."

Then Uncle Ben added, "I'll send another message at the same time. This one I'll seal up in a bottle and drop into the ocean. The waves of the old Atlantic will probably bring it ashore sometime. Perhaps right here at Sandy Cove. Who knows?"

The next day Captain Ben went away, but his ship did not sail until the twelfth of November. Jerry could scarcely wait for the radiogram to come. On the twelfth of November, about two o'clock, the telephone rang.

"Jerry, it's for you," said his mother.

The boy was so excited he could scarcely hold the telephone receiver. He heard the operator's voice say, "Radiogram for Jerry Frost." Then the radiogram was read to him.

"HELLO, JERRY. FINE WEATHER. UNCLE BEN."

Jerry wondered when the other message would come. Every day he hustled down to the beach to look for a bottle with a letter inside it. The first day he found a bottle, but it was empty. On the second day he found a tiny pear-shaped shell as smooth as satin.

On the third day he found a black-tipped gull's feather and a peculiar pink pebble. But no gull's feather, shell, or pebble could cause Jerry to forget the message that he looked for so anxiously.

One night there was a terrible storm. The Atlantic Ocean roared all night long, and the waves dashed on the beach. Jerry was up and at the shore soon after dawn.

"Now I shall find the bottle," he decided. "The old Atlantic will bring it this time."

Seaweed was scattered on the beach, and all kinds of queer things had been washed ashore, but there was no bottle.

"I don't believe it will ever come," said Jerry doubtfully. But he kept on looking.

About a month later, he went to the post office to get the mail. There was a letter for his father—and a package addressed to him! Jerry raced home all out of breath.

"Look," he shouted, almost swallowing his tongue in excitement. "I have a package mailed from Canada. Who sent it?"

"Open it and find out," urged Father with a chuckle.

Quickly Jerry tore open the cardboard box. Inside was a sealed bottle with a paper tag fastened to its neck. On the tag was written, "I picked up this bottle when I was out in my fishing boat. I'm mailing it to the person whose address is on the letter inside."

The tag was signed *Abraham Page*.

Unsealing the bottle, Jerry fished out the letter and read it aloud.

Dear Jerry,

It is noon on the twelfth of November, so here is the message I promised you when I was in Sandy Cove. I hope the person who finds it will mail it to you.

Love from Uncle Ben

"Well," said Jerry, "I'm glad Uncle Ben can send radiograms if his ship ever sinks. He'd wait a long time before a letter in a bottle could tell anyone he was shipwrecked."

# Steam Shovels Are Handy

## A Big Idea

Paul and Judy Tucker climbed up on the pasture fence to watch a big truck dumping small heaps of gravel along the roadside. Lady, their collie dog, stood beside them, hot and tired after a long walk.

"That gravel is a good idea," Paul said. "Now our car won't get stuck in those mud holes every time it rains."

The truck dumped its last heap of gravel, and as the driver started off, he called out, "That's all for this road."

"Aren't you going to fill the rest of the mud holes?" Paul called to him.

"I guess not, sonny," said the man. "We can't get any more gravel around here."

As the truck moved toward town, Judy and Paul jumped down off the fence and started to the creek that bordered their farm.

"I'm going wading," Judy said, pulling off her shoes and stockings. "It's hot."

"Wading is all right," Paul said. "But what we need is a swimming hole."

"A swimming hole!" Judy shouted.

"Whoof! Whoof!" barked Lady, waving her plumy tail in answer to Judy's shout. But her bark went unnoticed, because Judy's mind was busy with the idea of a swimming hole.

A dozen times they had attempted to dig a hole in the shallow creek, but the swirling water had filled up the hole with sand.

"What we *really* need," Paul said as they waded in the creek, "is a steam shovel to dig a hole deep enough for a person to swim in."

"I've got two dollars and forty cents in my bank," Judy offered. "Let's rent one."

"Pooh!" Paul sniffed. "It costs more than that to rent one. And we'd have to hire an operator, too. We couldn't hire an operator for even one day with your money."

"Hire an operator?" asked a laughing voice behind them. The two children turned to see their father pushing through the willow trees that bordered the creek.

"Why do you want to hire an operator?" continued Mr. Tucker.

"To run a steam shovel," said Judy.

"A steam shovel!" her father gasped.

"Yes, Dad," Paul explained. "That's the only way we can ever get a hole big enough for a swimming pool."

"Wh-whew!" whistled Mr. Tucker. "You youngsters certainly have big ideas. I—"

But just then he was interrupted by a swirl of sand and pebbles sent peppering over him by Lady's flying feet.

"Lady's after a ground hog," cried Paul. "Dig him out, Lady! Dig him out!"

On hearing her master's orders, Lady dug frantically, while sand and pebbles filled the air like hailstones.

"Well!" laughed Father, wiping the wet sand from his face. "Lady must think she's a steam shovel, the way she's throwing gravel out of that hole."

At the word *gravel*, a thoughtful look came into Paul's eyes. "Say, Dad!" he exclaimed. "Is there enough gravel here to fix a road?"

"I imagine there is," answered Mr. Tucker, "if it's good enough. Only a certain kind of gravel is used for roads, you know."

By now, Lady had decided that the ground-hog hole was empty. As she came prancing toward him, Mr. Tucker noticed the moist sand and pebbles clinging to her coat.

Bending over the hole, he plunged his arm in full-length and brought up a fistful of moist soil. He examined it closely. Then picking up a stick, he reached in and scraped out more soil from the bottom of the hole.

"This gravel is good," he said. "There's probably more of it beneath the creek."

"Would a man with a steam shovel dig it out and take the gravel for pay?" Paul asked breathlessly.

Mr. Tucker's eyes twinkled as he caught Paul's idea. "I happen to know Jim Thorn, the County Road Commissioner," he said. "Jim has a steam shovel, and he needs lots of gravel. We'll ask him about it tonight."

After the evening chores were done, the whole family got into their automobile and drove to the Road Commissioner's home.

Behind Jim Thorn's barn were all sorts of road-building machines. He had trucks that held ten tons, a road scraper with a curved blade for smoothing gravel, and best of all, a tremendous steam shovel.

Paul was bursting with questions about the shovel, and Mr. Thorn came out just in time to answer them.

"I call it a clam shell," he explained, "because the scoop closes just like a clam. Get into the cab, and I'll show you how it works."

Paul needed no urging. He followed Jim into the cab, while the others watched.

"That lever guides the big clam shell," Mr. Thorn continued. "This lever swings the long arm to the right or left, so that the load of gravel can be dumped wherever you want it. The clam shell picks up half a ton of gravel in just one bite of those tremendous jaws. So it fills a ten-ton truck with gravel pretty fast."

"Wait," said Mr. Tucker. "Our business is to ask about gravel. Do you need any?"

"Yes, indeed," replied Mr. Thorn. "When I'm working on the north side of the county, it's easy to get gravel from that big pit near Blednock River. But here on the south side there isn't a good gravel pit within easy hauling distance."

"We'll *give* you some gravel," Paul broke in, "right from the creek on our farm."

"We'll trade gravel for a swimming pool," Judy added. "We want one so much."

"These youngsters have a pretty smart idea," Mr. Tucker said. Then he explained the plan.

"Did you make a test hole to see if it is good gravel?" questioned Jim Thorn.

"No," said Mr. Tucker. "I only scraped a fistful from a ground-hog hole, but I think there's quite a lot of good gravel. Several hundred tons, at least."

"I'll test it," said the Commissioner.

"And you'll really take it?" begged Judy, her dark eyes snapping with eagerness.

"If it tests right, I will," he nodded. "I remember how much I wanted a swimming hole when I was a youngster."

## All in a Day's Work

On Thursday the Road Commissioner gave the necessary approval of the gravel. Then the steam shovel came clattering up the road, crossed the bridge, and stopped beside a clump of willows along the creek.

Paul and Judy watched the operator move the machine carefully, first forward and then in reverse, until the shovel was in the best place. Soon it began dipping its clam shell into the creek like some giant water bird hunting fish.

While the big shovel dipped its clam shell up and down, three trucks waited to be piled high with the moist gravel. When each truck was filled, it moved cautiously across the field, chugged along the road in a cloud of dust, and dumped its gravel.

As Jim Thorn gave directions, Paul and Judy watched the clam shell swing downward, scoop up a load of dripping gravel, and then swing to the reverse side to empty its load.

Barking excitedly, Lady watched the big clam shell rise and fall, while Paul and Judy greeted each new load with a chorus of shouts.

To Paul and Judy the most exciting thing was the way the swimming hole grew bigger with every bite of the clam shell's jaws.

"The water is a little muddy now," Mr. Thorn said. "But after we finish the job, you'll be able to see down to the bottom." Paul and Judy nodded, sure that it would be the best swimming hole in the entire county.

It was then that the accident happened.

Dodging to get out of the way of a truck, the frisky collie slipped into the deepest part of the pool. Just then the clam shell dipped into the creek for another load and struck the collie a sharp blow. Lady was a good swimmer, but the blow left her dazed and helpless. There she was, struggling feebly in the water.

"She'll drown!" came Judy's dismayed cry as the dazed collie was sinking beneath the surface.

Paul started to plunge in after his pet, but Jim Thorn shouted, "I'll save her!"

Big Jim leaped into the cab of the steam shovel, beside the operator. Cautiously he handled the levers. The long arm of the big shovel reached out above the drowning dog. Jim touched another lever. Down dipped the clam shell into the swirling water, and its jaws closed gently around Lady's body.

Then the clam shell was raised, and the long arm swung in reverse. In a moment the dripping collie was put on the bank, but everyone was afraid that she was dead.

Kneeling quickly beside the half-drowned collie, Paul moved the dripping front paws up and down. Mr. Thorn pressed in and out against the bones in Lady's sides. He pressed in and out with steady strokes to make the dog breathe again.

"Please save her!" Paul said, swallowing hard to keep back his tears. "Oh, Lady!"

Just then Lady's ears quivered, and she opened her eyes. Feebly she got to her feet. Giving a weak little whine, she wagged her dripping tail and licked Paul's hand.

Judy and Paul had never been so happy in their lives. Eager words of thanks tumbled from their lips.

"Oh, that's all right," Mr. Thorn said. "It's all in a day's work."

"I think," Paul said seriously, "that when I grow up I'm going to have a steam shovel and be a road commissioner, too."

"So you can dig a swimming hole when you want one?" Mr. Thorn asked jokingly.

"Well," Paul said, "not exactly. A steam shovel has more important jobs than that. It's a mighty handy thing to have around."

# Southbound Flight

## A Visit to the Airport

School was over for the day. Ted Johnson and his sister June hurried out, glad that the way home led past the airport. Five or six other pupils headed for the airport, too. Nearly every day they stopped for a few minutes to watch the big planes land and take off.

Ted and June raced along, eager to get there first and find a good place near the fence.

"Hurry, June," Ted urged. "Here comes the southbound plane now."

The southbound plane was their favorite, because their neighbor, Bill Huff, happened to be its pilot. Bill's co-pilot, Jack Burns, and Miss Case, the stewardess who looked after the passengers, were friendly, too.

Every Thursday the great passenger plane came in from the north, and Pilot Huff was always there to take it out again on its southbound flight to Texas. No matter how busy they were, Pilot Huff and the co-pilot and Miss Case always took time to give a special smile to the children.

"Here it comes," yelled Ted again as the silver plane circled downward. The children crowded against the wire fence in an excited cluster.

The plane nosed into the wind and came swooping down to the runway, the whirling blades of its propellers shining in the sun. Some of the passengers got out and walked around while mail sacks were being unloaded and the plane refueled.

"Southbound plane is now ready," came the announcement over the loud-speaker. "Southbound passengers go to Gate Two."

Ted and June were already just as close to Gate Two as they could get.

"Hi, Mr. Huff! Hi, Mr. Burns and Miss Case!" they chorused as the pilots and the stewardess went by.

Bill Huff and the passengers mounted the steps to the plane. Miss Case and the co-pilot followed them after checking all the names on the passenger list. Then the door was shut, and the steps were wheeled away.

An airport worker stepped forward and gave the signal to start. Pilot Huff saluted in answer, and the propellers began to whirl. The plane taxied slowly down the runway and began to rise easily from the ground.

Circling over the field, the silver ship headed south toward Texas. The children watched until it was lost to view among the clouds. "It's out of sight," Ted said at last. "Let's go."

Bert Allen joined Ted and June, and then the three friends started home through a small grove of trees. They walked along the narrow path, their feet swishing noisily through the leaves and grass. Ted plunged into a deep pile of fallen leaves, and the others followed, shouting and laughing.

As if in echo to their shouts, a chorus of hoarse cries came from a clump of maple trees. Whir, whir-r-r! went a hundred pairs of glossy, black wings as a flock of birds flew up into the air.

"Look! Look!" cried June.

"Blackbirds!" said Ted. "We talked about them in Scout meeting yesterday. They're gathering in flocks to fly south together. Most of the flocks have left by now."

Suddenly June gave a sharp cry and knelt down to look at something in the dry leaves. The others ran to kneel beside her.

## An Unhappy Guest

"It's a bird," said June, "but it can't fly."

"Maybe its wing is broken," Bert said.

"I'm going to take it home," June decided.

"Yes," said Ted. "It can't fly south, and we'll have snow before long."

June carried the blackbird cautiously in her hand, and it lay still, as if it were very tired. As soon as they reached home, the children took the bird to their father.

"Yes, indeed, we'll keep it," Mr. Johnson agreed, and he fixed up a wire cage where the bird would be comfortable.

The children named the blackbird Chirp. Not that he ever chirped, but because they wished he would. "Chirp," they would coax, tossing him grains of corn, but he always pecked away at the food without a sound.

144

By late November Chirp was more lively, but the bones in his wing were not strong enough for him to make a long flight.

"He'll have a hard time of it outdoors if we have a lot of snow and ice this winter," said Mr. Johnson. "Better keep him here in the cage. At least he'll be comfortable."

Chirp probably was comfortable in the cage, but he didn't look happy. He sat for hours at a time, huddled in one corner.

"You want to go south, don't you, Chirp?" Ted asked. "I wish I could help you."

And then all of a sudden Ted thought of a way he could help. When June heard about it, she was as excited as her brother.

After school the next day they hurried off to the airport faster than ever. Instead of going over to the fence by Gate Two, they went inside the office and talked to a man at the desk.

When they came out, the plane had gone, and most of the children had started home.

"Where have you been?" Bert Allen asked the latecomers. "You'd better try to be on time tomorrow. It's Pilot Huff's day to take the Southbound."

"We'll be here," Ted promised, "for more reasons than one!"

But no matter how hard Bert teased him, Ted wouldn't explain what he meant. Even June would only say, "Wait and see."

As soon as they reached home, Ted went to work cutting tiny holes in a big cardboard box. Bert Allen stayed to watch.

"What's that for?" he asked curiously.

"Wait and see," Ted replied with a grin.

The next afternoon when Ted and June came to school, they had the box, with a tag tied to it. Chirp was inside.

Bert was still curious. "What's going to happen to Chirp now?" he asked.

"He's going to fly south," Ted answered.

"But he can't," Bert insisted. "It's too far away for a bird with a lame wing."

"Not the way Chirp flies," Ted chuckled.

## A Special Passenger

As soon as school was out, the children raced to the airport. Bert was in such a hurry to get near the gate that he didn't notice Ted disappearing inside the office.

A few minutes later Ted came running up to the gate, just as the pilot and co-pilot and the stewardess passed by.

"Hi there, youngsters," called Pilot Huff, and Miss Case smiled and waved.

Bert's eyes widened in amazement. The stewardess was carrying Chirp's box!

"Special passenger!" said Miss Case as she passed June. "I'll let him out when I get to Texas. Or would you rather have me give him to the children who always meet me in Fort Worth, and let them turn him loose?"

"Oh, have them do it!" June said. "Will you take them a note if I write it?"

"I haven't time to wait for a note," the stewardess answered. "But I'll write your name and address on the tag."

Then she hurried off to check the passenger list and see that everyone was in his seat before the plane started southward.

At the last minute the stewardess turned to give an extra wave to the children. The steps were rolled away, and the propellers began to whirl. Pilot Huff returned the starter's salute, and the plane taxied down the runway.

The silver ship gathered speed and began to rise into the air as its propellers whirled faster. Chirp was flying southward at last.

"I wonder if we'll ever hear of him," Ted said as the plane vanished from sight.

Less than a week later a letter mailed in Fort Worth, Texas, arrived. It was addressed to June, and it contained news of Chirp.

Dear Friend,
The stewardess gave us the blackbird. We fed him bugs and worms and turned him loose.

Tony and Rosa

# A New Job for a Tractor

## A Serious Problem

"Get ready to feed our calves, Benny," Tom Aiken called as he drove the tractor out of the shed. "Dad says that we can use the tractor now to haul our hay. We'd better plan on feeding double rations. Those calves need extra feed to keep up their strength this cold weather."

Benny buttoned up his leather coat over his sweater and crossed the icy yard toward the tractor shed.

The weather had turned colder after a January rain, causing ice and snow to freeze on every tree, bush, and grass blade.

Icy snow lay in a thick, hard crust over the pasture where their two heifers were supposed to be grazing. If this bad weather continued all through January, how could Beauty and Buttercup ever get fat enough to win the prize at the county fair?

Benny knew those prize rules by heart. A prize of one hundred dollars would be given to the Willow County boy or girl, not over fifteen years old, who raised the best heifer at the lowest cost.

Lowest cost! That meant spending just as little as possible to buy feed. When there wasn't much snow, the heifers could graze in the pasture, and so feeding was cheap. But now with the grass hidden beneath an icy covering, hay and grain would have to be bought. The calves needed double rations, too, and the feed bill would go sky-high.

Tom bent over the tractor, checking fuel. "Get the heavy chain, Benny," he called over his shoulder. "We'll hook it to the bale of hay and have those heifers fed in less than no time. Br-r-r-r! I guess we ought to put Buttercup and Beauty in the warm barn."

"Oh, no," Benny answered. "Dad says a sudden change wouldn't be good for them. They'd be sure to stop eating for awhile, and then they'd lose weight. I wish we had decided to keep them inside all winter. Then they wouldn't need double rations."

"Well, don't worry," Tom advised. "The others in this contest can't feed any more cheaply than we do. Come along now."

With Tom driving the tractor and Benny riding astride the bale of hay, they started for the pasture. Benny was still wishing that they had never tried to leave the heifers out all winter so that their coats would be thick and glossy. For even the most glossy coats would not win a prize if the feed bill was too high.

As the tractor slowed down, Benny jumped off and ran ahead to open the pasture gate. Hammering the lock with his fist, he broke off the ice and swung the gate wide.

Ahead of them they saw their two black and white heifers. They were huddled close together against the hill that protected them from the fierce January wind.

"They're shivering," Tom said. "And see how they're huddled together."

"They're not even chewing their cuds," Benny declared. "If a cow isn't eating or chewing her cud, there's something wrong." He banged the gate shut and jumped astride the bale of hay again, as the heavy tractor went chugging off across the pasture.

Before they reached the hill, Tom stopped the tractor. Benny unhooked the chain and cut the wire on the bale of hay.

"Now the heifers will have to come out here to eat," he said.

Benny trotted ahead to drive the calves toward the hay, while Tom tried to start the tractor again. The motor gave a peculiar coughing sound, choked noisily, and then started up with a loud put-put-put.

Frightened by the sudden noise, the calves turned toward the tractor angrily. They stared at it in silence, their eyes dull red and their nostrils twitching.

As the tractor came nearer, they switched their tails and snorted in fear. Backing slowly, they stared with angry eyes at the chugging iron monster.

Suddenly Beauty backed into Buttercup. Both calves bellowed angrily and charged at each other, locking their tiny horns together.

"We can't let them fight!" Benny cried. "Separate them! If they hurt each other, we can't show them at the fair!"

"I'll drive the tractor toward them," Tom suggested. "That will separate them."

Tom was right. As the noisy engine came nearer, they separated and turned toward it. Tom put the tractor in reverse. Slowly he backed it away and stopped again. Beauty and Buttercup stamped and bellowed loudly.

"Hurry up," Benny yelled as he approached the heifers. "You're as slow as molasses in January. Get along and eat your breakfast."

He thumped Beauty on the back, and she ambled toward the hay. Buttercup ambled after her. Then as she passed the tractor, she dodged aside, rolling her eyes comically.

"Now we've another job to do," said Tom. "We must make a real shelter for the calves." He pointed to clumps of bushes bordering one end of the pasture. "We'll drive the tractor over there, hook the chain around them, and jerk them out by the roots. That brushwood will make good, thick walls, and those two walnut trees are in just the right places for end posts. We'll stack brushwood from each walnut tree to the hill. Then the heifers will have shelter on three sides—north, east, and west. It will be warmer for them, and they'll still be outdoors."

Benny's face glowed. "Great idea, Tom! Now if we could only figure out some way to get rid of this ice, so that they could graze, they'd be all right. I wish I could wave a fairy wand and start a warm wind!"

Benny and Tom went to work, uprooting the brushwood and dragging it over to the walnut trees. Then they began weaving and pressing the branches together. Soon a windbreak would stretch thick and strong from each walnut tree to the hill.

## A Surprising Answer

When at last the shelter was completed, Tom said, "Well, let's go. We've done the best we could for the heifers."

With Tom on the tractor seat and Benny standing behind him, the boys started for the gate. They saw that the heifers were no longer huddling together, but seemed to be snuffing along the ground. As the boys came nearer, they realized that the calves were paying no attention to the hay. They were munching something just beside it.

"What do you suppose they're doing?" Benny asked in a puzzled tone.

The tractor crawled closer to the calves.

"Look!" Tom whooped joyfully. "See what those heifers are eating! We've got the answer to the double-rations problem!"

Benny stared, at first unbelieving, then with rising excitement. The two heifers were munching the sweet pasture grass that had been uncovered where the heavy tractor had rolled over the ground.

The weight of the rough tractor wheels had broken up the icy crust. The bale of hay dragging behind the tractor had pushed the ice aside, and now the heifers could get at the grass.

"Hurrah!" Benny whooped. "Let's hook a log to the chain. Its weight will help break ice and sweep it aside, too. We can break ice every time it freezes. You can depend on a tractor to do a good job, all right!"

All forenoon the boys worked, while the heifers grazed or contentedly chewed their cuds. To the happy boys, the prize for low-cost calves seemed as good as won.

# When the Lights Failed

Tomorrow would be Henry Stoner's birthday, and for the first time it would take two figures to tell his age. Today he was nine, but tomorrow he would be ten.

Henry sat on the porch, munching cookies and trying to decide what he would choose for a special birthday treat. He had been promised that he could do anything he wished—anything within reason, of course.

He had thought of going fishing with his father. But his father was a doctor, and yesterday Dr. Stoner had been called to see a patient in another state. So there was no chance for a fishing trip.

"I'll take a plane both ways," his father had promised. "Then I can get back for the last few hours of your birthday, at least."

The thought of his father's flying home on the big mainliner gave Henry an idea.

"Oh, Mother!" he called, jumping up and running into the kitchen. "I know what I'll choose for my birthday treat. I want to go to the airport and watch for Dad's plane."

His mother hesitated at his announcement.

"It will be dark, Henry," she said, "and Father's plane doesn't stop at our airport, you know. He has to go on to the big airport at Chicago and come back by train."

"Yes, I know," Henry said. "But I'll see his plane go over. It always signals with its lights when it's above the airport."

"Well—," his mother hesitated doubtfully.

"You promised that I may do anything I choose," Henry reminded her.

"All right," Mrs. Stoner granted with a smile. "A promise is a promise."

The next evening Henry was ready to leave for the airport right after supper.

"Please be careful," advised his mother. "And come back just as soon as the Chicago plane has gone over."

Henry promised, and off he hurried to the airport, only a short distance away. He had been there often in the daytime, but this was his first visit alone at night.

As he approached the airport, he saw the runways bordered by rows of lights set even with the surface of the ground.

Great clusters of floodlights made the landing field almost as bright as day. A sharp thrill of excitement ran up and down Henry's backbone, the way it always did when he saw the field.

He had visited the airport often enough to know that an airplane has to land and take off against the wind. He looked up at the windsock puffing out like a balloon above the office building. The wind was coming from the north. This meant that a plane would have to approach the field from the south.

Sure enough, at the entrance to the south runway a green light glowed, showing pilots exactly where to land.

Henry hurried into the manager's office.

"You're just in time," Mr. Thresher said. "The big mainliner to Chicago will land here tonight. The pilot just radioed that something has gone wrong with the motors. We're all lighted up, ready for him."

Hardly had he finished speaking, when out went all the lights, leaving the field and office in complete darkness. It happened so suddenly that both the boy and the man gave a jump. Then Joe Thresher clicked the signal switch on the radio to call the pilot who was nearing the field.

"Larry," he warned, "keep circling for a couple of minutes until I put in a new fuse."

"Hurry, Joe!" answered the pilot's voice out of the loud-speaker. "I don't know how long my motors will run."

Joe grabbed his flashlight and rushed to the light switches. It took only a minute to find the trouble and put in a new fuse.

Overhead they could hear the dull hum of the plane, interrupted by the noisy choking of a motor. As the lights flashed on again, Henry's heart gave a wild leap, and Joe grunted in satisfaction.

Then out went the lights a second time.

The manager mumbled something about fuses and worked frantically at the switches. All of a sudden there came a bright flash— then complete darkness. Joe fell to the floor and lay there limp and motionless.

"Mr. Thresher!" screamed the frightened boy. But he called to unhearing ears. A fault in the wiring had caused an electric charge to pass through the man's body instead of flowing down the wires and lighting the buildings and field. Joe had received an electric shock, but he was still breathing.

What was Henry to do? He had learned a few first-aid rules as a Cub Scout, but he had to choose between aiding Joe and helping the plane that carried his father.

The sound of the choking motor was louder now. Henry decided that even if its motors held out, the big plane might run out of gas before it could find a landing place in the dark. He didn't know just what to do, but he was sure that the plane would crash unless something was done immediately.

Henry picked up the flashlight and saw that Joe's nostrils were twitching. He was still alive. Quickly Henry found Joe's coat and covered his still form. Just then the pilot's voice came from the loud-speaker.

"Where are the lights, Joe? Where are the lights? Hurry up, man!"

Henry hesitated no longer. He clicked the radio signal switch as Joe had done. "Larry!" he shouted into the mouthpiece. "Something's wrong with the fuses. Joe got an electric shock. Keep going for a few minutes, and I'll try to get some lights."

Without waiting to know whether Larry had received his message, Henry took the flashlight and hurried out. Once outside, he raced to a gas station that stood on the highway near the airport entrance.

163

One car had just been filled with gas, and several others were waiting there in line.

"Wait! Wait!" Henry shouted, waving Joe's flashlight frantically as the first car started away. All the drivers looked up.

"The plane! The Chicago plane!" Henry yelled. "It can't land. The lights are out. Light the field with your headlights."

The drivers heard the motor cough and sputter overhead and started for the airport.

"I'll send over every car that comes along," called the gas-station operator as the cars headed for the field.

Henry had jumped into the first car to guide the drivers to the runway where the green light had shown. The cars formed in clusters along the runway so that the headlights completely flooded the path.

The plane circled downward, its motors coughing and sputtering feebly. A moment later, like a great bird, it swooped down to the runway and taxied to a stop.

One after another the passengers stepped out. Henry saw the co-pilot explaining the trouble to them, while the stewardess made sure everyone was all right. Then Henry's searching eyes recognized a tall, familiar figure.

"Dad! Dad!" he called frantically as he rushed forward.

Greatly surprised, Dr. Stoner hastened to his son's side.

"Hurry, Dad," urged Henry, pulling his father over to the office. "Mr. Thresher needs a doctor. He's had an electric shock."

Aided by the flashlight, they soon found the manager's motionless form. Kneeling quickly, Dr. Stoner listened to Joe's heart and felt his cool, moist skin. Henry could see Joe's feebly twitching nostrils, and he knew that the manager was still alive.

"He'll be all right," Dr. Stoner said. "He is lucky it wasn't a more dangerous shock."

When the pilot discovered all that Henry had done, he praised the boy for saving the plane from a serious accident.

"You're a plucky boy," Larry said, and the passengers echoed his praise.

"The car lights saved you. I didn't," Henry said, but they insisted on thanking him and almost shook his hand off.

"Whew!" he said to his father as they finally started home. "I'll never forget this birthday! I've had more excitement than on all my other birthdays put together."

# Story-Land
# of Here and Now

# The Wizard of Vilville

## The Wizard Arrives

From all directions the people of Vilville came running to the town notice board. A most unusual notice was on it!

GOOD PEOPLE, TAKE NOTICE

I shall come to VILVILLE on Thursday noon.

I have disguised myself as a rabbit.

I SHALL BE VERY HUNGRY.

The first person who feeds me shall be granted

a PECULIAR POWER until six o'clock.

(Signed) THE WIZARD OF VILVILLE

No one was sure what the Peculiar Power might be, but everyone was certain it would be magic and quite nice.

Long before noon on Thursday the crooked road that led into Vilville was lined with eager people, their arms full of wizard food.

And right at noon, down the road came scampering a little bunny. Now this was just an ordinary rabbit, looking for a scrap of something to nibble. But the people didn't know that. They were sure he was the disguised Wizard, and they began tossing him things to eat.

When the bunny looked up, he saw apples, carrots, beets, tender young turnips, small squashes, and even lamb chops come flying at him. Off he went as fast as a rabbit could hop. After him streamed the entire crowd.

Not a soul was left in the village, that is, no one except old Auntie Grumble, who was a most unpleasant person.

To begin with, she didn't believe in the Wizard at all or in magic of any sort. There she was, left alone in her crooked house, complaining to herself as usual.

"All that uproar!" she sputtered.

Mumbling and grumbling to herself, old Auntie hobbled out to her front gate.

"And just see that!" she complained. "Here's a carrot some careless person has dropped."

And very angrily she threw the carrot as far down the road as she could.

Meanwhile the Wizard, disguised as a rabbit, was hopping slowly into the village, wondering what on earth had happened to the villagers. He looked about him amazed, for the houses and streets were empty.

Not a soul did he see. It actually seemed as if nobody cared whether he came to town or not. He was beginning to feel annoyed.

He hopped along, growing more and more annoyed at every step. He was about to become hopping mad!

"So that's how it is!" he muttered. "If they don't care any more for me than this, I will go away and never do another bit of magic for them, not ever, ever again.

"Here I am—nearly starving, and—"
WH-OP!

The Wizard leaped into the air as Auntie Grumble's great big carrot hit him right between the ears.

Hungrily the Wizard fell upon that carrot and began munching it, forgetting how vexed he had been a moment before. As the last sweet bit slid down his red throat, he wiped his whiskers, twitched his nose, and went hopping to Auntie Grumble's crooked house. There he found her, frowning and scolding.

The Wizard bowed until his ears touched the floor.

"Many thanks, good lady, for the delicious food!" he said to her very politely.

Auntie Grumble looked up cautiously and squinted her eyes at him.

"Who are you?" she demanded loudly.

"What do I look like?" asked the Wizard.

"You look like a rabbit, of course!"

"Good!" said the Wizard of Vilville with satisfaction. "I have disguised myself as a rabbit purposely to look like one."

"Oh," said Auntie, "you must be—" She started to say, "the Wizard," but she did not, because she did not believe in wizards.

"Yes, lady, I am the Wizard of Vilville!" announced the rabbit proudly. He bowed low again before her. "Now I'll grant you the Peculiar Power, as advertised on the town notice board. GIZZICK! GIZZOCK! GIZZOOK! There, my good lady, you have it."

"Have what?" asked the old woman.

"The Peculiar Power. From now on until six o'clock, if you *say* it is—*it is!*

"Just remember that you have the Peculiar Power and remember to use it wisely. Now I must be hopping along. Good day!"

## The Power Works

"What on earth did that rabbit mean?" said Auntie Grumble when the Wizard had gone ka-hop, ka-hopping out of sight.

She muttered the Wizard's words over and over. "If I *say* it is—*it is!* Such talk! Well, if I have any Peculiar Power, it isn't hurting me. Now I must get the broom and sweep the floor. Ugh! *Rabbits all over the house like this!*"

Old Auntie Grumble stopped suddenly and began screaming, "Eeee! Eeee! Eeee!"

For in just that moment the house *was* full of rabbits, just as she had said—although she hadn't meant exactly that, really. But she had *said* it. And now what was she to do with all these rabbits?

Here they were, hopping madly all over the place. Auntie seized her broom and began waving it wildly about, chasing the rabbits out of the house.

Poor Auntie sat down panting and gasping. "Whatever made that happen?" she said, fanning herself with her apron. "Just look at my hands after chasing all those dirty animals under the furniture. I'll have to wash them—*they are simply black!*"

Ugh! What a funny feeling came creeping over her hands! She looked at them quickly, and then even more quickly she hid them under her apron. Then she gave a careless glance at the ceiling, pretending to herself that she had not seen anything unusual at all. But just the same she was terribly startled, for her hands certainly were black!

Meanwhile the citizens were coming back into town, looking sorrowful.

Auntie Grumble leaned out of her window. "Hmph!" she said crossly. "They ought to hurry home, where they belong. The sky looks cloudy. *It'll be raining cats and dogs in a minute.*"

Sixty seconds passed.

And then the air was suddenly full of tiny furry and hairy bodies, that came peppering down to the ground, crying, "Yipe! Yipe!" and "Meow! Meow!" and "Ffft! Ffft!" and "Bow-wow-wow!"

It was actually raining cats and dogs!

The uproar was awful. Everyone hurried for shelter, holding his hands over his ears to keep out the terrible noise those live raindrops were making. They bounced to the ground, rolled over one another, barked, meowed—and kept right on coming down!

The old woman who had caused it all found herself jumping up and down in her excitement. Before she realized it, she was saying, "*No, it isn't!  It isn't raining anything!*"

Ssssh! The awful noise stopped just as suddenly as it had begun, and not a single other cat or dog or kitten or pup fell from the sky.

## Auntie Changes Her Ways

Now Auntie Grumble sat down to fan herself and think it over. There was no use to deny it any longer. She certainly had a Peculiar Power! And who had given it to her but the rabbit that had called himself the Wizard of Vilville?

Well, well! Maybe it was true, after all.

But how should she use the Power wisely, as the rabbit had advised?

Auntie rocked and puffed and winked and snuffed and tapped her toes and wrinkled her nose and tried to think. It was perfectly true that she was an unhappy old woman. She was so cross that no one dared speak to her. Suddenly she had the feeling that she wanted to be happy. "Well, why not?" she thought. "If I *say* it is—*it is!*" She leaped up, folded her arms, then stood quite still and said, "*I am very happy!*"

Auntie Grumble felt so light-hearted and brand-new, somehow, that she found herself laughing right out loud. She laughed and shook and shook and laughed, and all the frown-wrinkles on her face began to crack into pieces and fall to the ground with curious little ting-a-ling sounds.

She kept on laughing until the windows of the house began to jiggle and jingle and the shingles on the roof started slapping and clapping. Even the birds began to sing in time to the funny little music-dance that was going on. Children began peeking over the gate, and older people came cautiously to see what all this odd music was about.

And now came the greatest surprise of that amazing day.

"Good afternoon, dear neighbors!" said Auntie Grumble most cheerfully. She had finally stopped laughing, but her face was still sweet and merry. "While you were off chasing a mere woods bunny, the Wizard came to my house, disguised as a rabbit."

"Oh-h-h!" gasped the dazed people.

"By the merest chance," went on Auntie, "I was the first to feed him. In return for a single carrot, he granted me the Peculiar Power! And he told me to use it wisely."

Auntie smiled guiltily as she confessed, "I—I guess I haven't used it very wisely. You see, I made it rain cats and dogs a little while ago, but not on purpose. That was quite an accident. And look! This was an accident, too!" She stretched out her hands for the people to see, and of course both of them were still coal black.

"I will show you how the Power works, if you like. See! *My hands are white!*"

In a flash the black vanished, and her hands were white again.

"Ah! Wonderful! Wonderful!" chorused the people.

"But now, my friends," went on Auntie, "I've thought of a way to use the Peculiar Power wisely, as the Wizard told me to do. If you will just hurry up and tell me your troubles, I'll do my best to make you all happy. You may have anything you desire. But please do not delay, because it's nearly six o'clock."

The people all began chattering at once, each demanding to be the first one to talk. They were all trying to discover a lot of troubles for her to set right, and they made a terrible uproar about it.

It took them so long to become orderly that suddenly Auntie threw up her hands in dismay. "Oh! Oh!" she cried. "It is six o'clock, and the Peculiar Power is—is— Oh, dear! It *isn't* any more! It was to last only till six o'clock!"

She fumbled for her apron and began to wipe her eyes, for big tears were rolling from them.

The startled people turned pale and began to whisper worriedly among themselves. What had they done?

Then a plump old man with tufted white whiskers stepped out of the crowd and made his way to Auntie Grumble's side.

"Now, now, now! Cheer up, good folks!" he urged in a most jolly tone. "There's no need to look so miserable. The Wizard has been here, just as advertised, and aren't we happy over that?"

"Well—yes," confessed the people, a little doubtfully.

"And really," the old man went on, "can you deny the fact that not a single soul here has any trouble worth mentioning? So how could the Peculiar Power give us any more satisfaction than we now have? Why, the only thing in Vilville that needed a little fixing was Auntie Grumble's grumble. And look at her now! She's the sweetest and the gentlest old lady you ever saw."

The people looked. They smiled. They began to laugh with pleasure. And all of a sudden they were cheering for pleasant old Auntie Gentle, who had always been called Auntie Grumble.

# The Huckabuck Family

Jonas Jonas Huckabuck was a farmer in Nebraska with a wife, Mama Mama Huckabuck, and a daughter, Pony Pony Huckabuck.

"Your father gave you two names the same in front," people had said to him.

And he answered, "Two names are easier to remember. If you call me by my first name, Jonas, and I don't hear you, then when you call me by my second name, Jonas, maybe I will.

"And," he went on, "I call my pony-face girl Pony Pony because, if she doesn't hear me the first time, she does the second."

So they lived on a farm where they raised popcorn, these three, Jonas Jonas Huckabuck, his wife, Mama Mama Huckabuck, and their pony-face daughter, Pony Pony Huckabuck.

After they harvested the crop one year, they had the barns, the cribs, the sheds, the shacks, and all the cracks and corners of the farm filled with popcorn.

"We came to Nebraska to raise popcorn," said Jonas Jonas, "and I guess we got nearly enough popcorn this year for all the popcorn poppers in these United States."

This year Pony Pony was going to bake her first squash pie by herself. She carried the squash into the kitchen, took a long, sharp, shining knife, and then she cut the squash in the middle till she had two big half-squashes. And inside, just like outside, it was rich yellow, spotted with gold.

There was a shine of silver, and Pony Pony wondered why silver should be in a squash. She picked and plunged with her fingers till she pulled it out. "It's a buckle!" she said. "A Chinese silver slipper buckle!"

She called to her father and said, "Look! See what I found when I cut open the golden yellow squash spotted with gold spots. It is a Chinese silver slipper buckle."

"It means our luck is going to change, and we don't know whether it will be good luck or bad luck," said Jonas Jonas to his daughter, Pony Pony Huckabuck.

That night a fire started in the barns, cribs, sheds, shacks, cracks, and corners, where the popcorn harvest was kept. All night long the popcorn popped. In the morning the ground around the farmhouse and the barn was all covered with popcorn so it looked like a heavy fall of snow.

All next day the fire kept on, and the popcorn popped till it was up to the shoulders of Pony Pony when she tried to walk from the house to the barn.

And that night in all the barns, cribs, sheds, shacks, cracks, and corners of the farm, the popcorn went on popping. In the morning when Jonas Jonas Huckabuck looked out of the upstairs window, he saw the popcorn popping and coming higher and higher. It was nearly up to the window.

Before evening and dark of that day, Jonas Jonas Huckabuck and his wife, Mama Mama Huckabuck, and their daughter, Pony Pony Huckabuck, all went away from the farm.

They went away saying, "We came to Nebraska to raise popcorn, but this is too much. We will not come back till we get a sign and a signal."

They went to another state. And that year Pony Pony Huckabuck was very, very proud. She was proud because, when she stood on the sidewalks, she could see her father sitting high on the seat of a coal wagon, driving two big spanking horses hitched with shining brass harness in front of the coal wagon.

And though Pony Pony and Jonas Jonas were proud, very proud, all that year, there never came a sign, a signal.

They went to many other states. And in all these places Pony Pony Huckabuck saw her father, Jonas Jonas Huckabuck, standing in rubber boots deep down in a ditch with a shining steel shovel, shoveling yellow clay and black mud from down in a ditch high up over his shoulders. And though they had proud years, they got no sign, no signal.

Then came the proudest year of all. This was the year Jonas Jonas was a watchman in a watch factory, watching the watches. And in the evenings Pony Pony would go down to the factory and watch her father watch the watches in the watch factory.

Thanksgiving came. Pony Pony said, "I am going to get a squash to make a squash pie."

She hunted from one grocery to another. She found what she wanted, a yellow squash spotted with gold spots. She took it home, cut it open, and saw the inside was like the outside, all rich yellow, spotted with gold.

There was a shine like silver. She picked and plunged with her fingers and pulled and pulled till at last she pulled out the shine of silver.

"It is a sign. It is a signal," she said. "It is a buckle, a slipper buckle, a Chinese silver slipper buckle. It is the mate to the other buckle. Our luck is going to change!"

She told her father and mother about the Chinese silver slipper buckle, and they all went back to the farm in Nebraska.

The wind by this time had been blowing and blowing for three years, and all the popcorn was blown away.

"Now we are going to be farmers again," said Jonas Jonas Huckabuck to Mama Mama Huckabuck and to Pony Pony Huckabuck. "We are going to raise cabbages, beets, and turnips. We are going to raise squash, pumpkins, and peppers. We are going to raise wheat. We are going to raise corn. But we are *not* going to raise any popcorn for the popcorn poppers to be popping."

Sometimes on Thanksgiving and Christmas and New Year's Pony Pony Huckabuck tells her friends to be careful when they open a squash.

"Squashes make your luck change good to bad and bad to good," says Pony Pony.

# The Princess Who Could Not Cry

There was once a princess who could not cry. That wouldn't have mattered so very much, but the trouble was that she laughed about everything, and often at the most awkward times. This was truly a vexing way to behave, especially for a princess.

Her parents were greatly troubled about it, and at last they called in a wise woman to advise them. She studied the problem thoughtfully and finally told them that if the Princess could only once be made to cry, the spell would be broken and she would then be as natural as other people.

The King and Queen immediately set about the task of making the Princess weep. This was a rather difficult matter, because they didn't want to make her really miserable. And since they could not bear to slap or spank her, they hardly knew how to begin.

Finally they advertised a reward of five hundred gold coins for anyone who could succeed in making their daughter cry without harming her or making her uncomfortable.

Wise men came from everywhere to see what they could do. They attempted many things, but all without success.

One man suggested that the Princess be locked up in a room by herself and fed on nothing but bread and water. The Queen thought this was very cruel, but at length the King persuaded her to try it.

This plan failed to make the Princess feel miserable enough to cry. Every time a servant brought her a bowl of bread and water, he found her laughing. At the end of two weeks she was pale, but still cheerful.

"See," she said, jiggling one tiny foot, "my feet have grown so thin that I can't keep my slippers on." She kicked the slipper across the room as she spoke, laughing merrily at the astonished face of the servant.

When the Queen saw the girl's bony hands and her thin, stilt-like legs, she burst into tears. "My poor, starved darling," she cried. And rushing into the kitchen, she ordered that peaches and cream and a big cake with chocolate sauce be served to the Princess to tempt her appetite.

A second wise man came and said that for sixty days he had practiced making fearful, crooked faces in order to scare the Princess into tears. He was left alone with her, while the Queen waited outside and listened anxiously.

But in a few minutes she heard peals of laughter coming from inside the room, and soon the wise man opened the door. His face was as red as a beet from the efforts he had been making.

"It's useless," he confessed, looking much annoyed.

Meanwhile the Princess was laughing with glee. "What a comical man!" she said. "Ask him to wrinkle up his face again."

Another wise man suggested that all her favorite toys should be broken. But when he went up to her room and began smashing her beautiful dolls and playthings, the Princess clapped her hands gleefully.

"How jolly!" she cried, and began tossing cushions and other things carelessly about. So that plan failed, too.

Other wise men came. But many of their suggestions were cruel ones, such as spanking and whipping. So naturally the King and Queen would not agree. They began to fear that all their efforts to make their darling child weep were wasted.

Now in a small village on the borders of the King's great royal park, there lived a poor woman with her daughter Marigold.

Marigold knew all about the Princess at the palace. And one morning as she was preparing breakfast, an idea came to her. As soon as the meal was over, she put on her hood and cloak and told her mother that she was going up to the palace to try to make the Princess cry, and so earn the reward.

Her mother tried to coax her to give up her plan. "How can you hope to succeed," she said, "especially since all the clever people in the kingdom have failed? It is useless for you to attempt such a task."

But Marigold was determined. So at last her mother gave up all efforts to persuade her to change her mind. And Marigold bravely set off for the palace, with a small covered basket over her arm.

Approaching the great front door, she felt frightened. But she thought of the reward, and standing on tiptoe, she pulled the bell handle so hard that she was startled at the tremendous noise.

One of the King's footmen opened the door. When he saw Marigold there in her plain-looking clothes, with a basket in her hand, he looked astonished. "Back entrance!" he said gruffly, and shut the door in her face without asking her purpose in coming.

So Marigold went to the back entrance. This time the door was opened by a maid. "We've nothing to give away," she said, and she, too, was about to close the door.

But the Queen was there in the kitchen, choosing the fresh vegetables that the King especially preferred for dinner.

"What do you wish, my child?" she asked.

"I've come to make the Princess cry, Your Majesty," said Marigold, making a curtsey.

The Queen shook her head, wondering how a mere village girl could hope to make a better suggestion than the fifty or sixty wise men had been able to make.

But Marigold was so serious and so sure she could make the Princess cry that at last the Queen was persuaded to let her attempt it. She was led to the Princess at once and left alone with her.

The Princess was delighted. She preferred to see this rosy-cheeked girl instead of the ridiculous, dull old men who had tried so often to make her weep.

By this time the news of the village girl who had come to make the Princess cry had spread over the palace. And presently a crowd of curious people had collected and were anxiously waiting outside the door.

"It's such nonsense," sniffed old Duke Proudheart. "A mere child! I don't suppose she's ever been outside the village."

"Quite ridiculous," whispered the royal ladies in the palace. "She won't even know how to make a correct curtsey."

At last the King and Queen could bear the
silence no longer.  They quietly opened the
door and peeped in.  There was the Princess,
standing at a table, with Marigold's basket
before her.  In the basket were—onions!
The Princess was peeling them as fast as she
could, tears streaming down her face all the
while.  She was crying at last!

The King and Queen rushed in and folded
their darling in their arms, onions and all.
The royal ladies stood with their perfumed
handkerchiefs pressed to their noses.  The
page boys giggled, and the cook muttered
to himself, "Onions!  Why wasn't I smart
enough to think of onions?"

# Three and Three

Once there lived in the country a Rabbit, a Dachshund, and a Cow.

The Rabbit liked to roam all over the hills and fields, looking for carrots and cabbages and other good things to eat. He had a tremendous appetite.

The Dachshund lived in a fine house, and he had everything a dog could ask for—toys, bones, and a bow around his neck. But he preferred to be outdoors.

The Cow spent all her time in a pasture, just chewing her cud and thinking. And every night before she went to sleep, she would listen for a wonderful sound that came from the treetops—it was an owl hooting.

The Rabbit had tasted every cabbage and carrot nearby. They all seemed alike, and he was tired of them. So one day he roamed very far away to find something new to eat.

Instead he found two strange animals with very long necks and very long legs. They were nibbling the leaves high up in a tree. They were giraffes.

The Rabbit wondered if those leaves would taste better than cabbages or carrots. Oh, if *he* only had a long neck to reach up to the high, tempting branches!

That same day the Dachshund went for a walk to the pond. There he spent hours and hours, watching the ducks. If only *he* could swim and dive like a duck, that was just what he would do.

That night the Cow listened for the hooting of the owl and saw that it could fly.

"How perfect," she thought, "to have wings and see beyond the pasture!"

One bright morning they all woke up and discovered that their wishes had come true.

The Rabbit discovered he was a GIRabbit. The Dachshund found he was a DUCKhund. And the Cow had turned into a COWL.

The GIRabbit nibbled leaves from a tall tree. They tasted very good, indeed, but— the GIRabbit couldn't jump any more without taking a bad tumble. And when he thought he was hidden in a bramble patch, he really wasn't! Even half a GIRabbit will not fit into a burrow. So when it began to thunder and lightning, he had to stay out in the rain.

The DUCKhund went to the pond and caught three fishes and two frogs. But when the ducks saw him in the water, they all gathered around and made fun of him. So he stayed out of the pond and dug up an old bone. But he found that ducks can't eat bones, and that made him very, very cross.

The COWL flew to the nearest telephone pole to see the view. But she was so excited that she didn't think about her horns, and they got all tangled up in the wires.

She finally got to the top of a tree and tried to hoot like the owl, but since she was still half cow, she found that she could only *moot*. She was very disappointed. So she stopped *mooting* and enjoyed the view immensely.

When night came, the COWL tried to sleep, but she couldn't. You see, an owl sleeps by day and is awake all night.

One day some gentlemen from the circus heard about these odd animals and set out to catch them and bring them back alive to show to all the world.

But the GIRabbit, the DUCKhund, and the COWL didn't want to be caught. When they saw the men coming, they ran away and hid in the woods.

Then the gentlemen from the circus dug a pit and in it laid a huge net. They left choice carrots, beets, fishes, chops, clover, and a catnip mouse to tempt them all.

Night came, and the three animals smelled the good food, which made them very, very hungry. They didn't see the pit and fell right into the net.

They spent a terrible night in the net, worrying and worrying, for they knew they would be taken to the circus and be put in cages and everybody would stare at them. They would never again be free.

Remember, if you *really* wish for something, it may happen!

So all night long they wished and wished more than anything else in the world that they could again be just plain, everyday animals.

Next day the gentlemen from the circus came back with a big cage. They pulled out the net to open it—and what did they find? Nothing but three plain, everyday animals!

The circus men were so furious to see just an ordinary rabbit, a dachshund, and a cow that they let them all go free.

And how they did run! Straight back to the fine home, the pasture, the carrots, and the cabbages!

# King Peramund's Wish

## A Bargain Is Made

It was at breakfast that King Peramund made his surprising remark. Squinting his eyes thoughtfully, he said, "I have been thinking lately that it would be nice if I possessed the art of flying like a bird."

"How ridiculous!" remarked the Queen as she peppered a soft-boiled egg. "What for?"

"Well, my dear," said the King, "there are several reasons. One is that it would be faster and more comfortable than riding in a coach. Another is that it would be something that not every king can do.

"A third reason is that I could fly right in at my window without climbing all those stairs. And, best of all, it would be fun."

"Well," said the Queen, "how are you going to accomplish it?"

"Really, my dear, I don't quite know," confessed the King. "It is merely an idea of mine. I don't know if it can be done, but I shall certainly find out."

After breakfast the King locked himself in his room. An hour later he came out with an announcement written on a long strip of paper and addressed to his people.

### KING PERAMUND TO HIS LOYAL PEOPLE

Whereas, We have Decided that it would be to our Good and the Good of all the loyal People of the Kingdom if we were to learn the difficult Art of Flying:

We hereby order that if any Person whatsoever shall possess the Power to teach this Art, he shall come to the King at once, who will grant said Person whatsoever Reward he shall demand.

Then the King had the notice hung on the royal palace gate, where all the people in his kingdom could read it.

Early next day the entrance bell pealed loudly. When the doorman opened the door, there stood an odd-looking woman in a black robe and hood. Entering the throne room, she made a stiff curtsey. Then she said in a croaking voice, "I possess the power to teach you the art of flying."

King Peramund jumped up from his throne. "Come, don't lose a moment," he panted.

The woman stood motionless and stared at him so long that he shuffled his feet uneasily. Then she said, "Will you grant me anything I wish, just as you advertised?"

"Anything!" he cried, jiggling and twitching in excitement. "You can depend on it."

"Very well!" said the woman, and waving her wand over him, she muttered a few words.

"Now," she said, "I demand that you give your oldest daughter to be the bride of the goblin who lives beneath the hill."

"My gracious!" cried the King. "I can't possibly do that, because—"

"Ah!" interrupted the woman. "So kings don't keep bargains! Well, I do. You shall fly, as I have said. But you won't like it."

With that, she gave a shriek and sailed out the window without even a curtsey.

Naturally the King was rather startled, but he thought that perhaps this was the usual way for such persons to take their leave. Her last remark had puzzled him, but she had said he could fly. So why should he worry?

### The King Begins to Fly

The King climbed on to the throne, bent his knees, and jumped. To his delight, he rose gracefully into the air and found himself up at the ceiling. He swooped gently down, bounced off the floor, and glided up again.

Then he pushed away from the ceiling and sailed through an open window and out over the palace courtyard. When he looked down, he grew dizzy. He gasped and shut his eyes and then flew back to the window.

When his dizzy spell had passed, Peramund gained enough courage to rise in the air again. He soared above the roofs, his coattails flapping gracefully in the breeze and his sword swishing along behind him.

Sometime later the Queen was having her morning cup of chocolate in bed. Suddenly a shadow swept across her window, and in flew Peramund. The Queen shrieked as the King swept in dizzy circles above her, the steel blade of his sword narrowly missing her head.

"What shall I do?" cried the King.

"About what?" cried the Queen, dodging.

"Don't you see?" said His Royal Majesty. "I've started to fly, and I can't stop!"

At this the Queen burst into whoops and peals of laughter. This so annoyed the King that he darted out the window again and flew miserably around the highest tower.

Here he was seen sometime later by the Captain of the Royal Guards and by the Queen, who now realized what a serious difficulty the King was in. She knew he had been enchanted.

Catching sight of her, the King bellowed, "What shall I do? Tell me something to do."

"Hold on to the weather vane!" the Queen advised. "And keep up your courage."

So the King grabbed the big brass rooster on top of the weather vane.

There was a great crash as the vane broke, and off flew Peramund, hugging the rooster. He dropped it in the courtyard beneath him.

"Whatever am I to do?" he shouted. "I can't keep flying around here forever!"

"Oh, I dare say you could, Your Majesty," replied the Captain of the Royal Guards. "But it's stopping that's so very difficult to accomplish. It's a very vexing problem."

After that the King flew around in silence for a time. But he grew chilly and began coughing and sneezing. To prevent his catching cold, the Queen brought his overshoes, overcoat, and plumed hat and held them out to him as he flew by a window. He really looked comical putting them on in the air.

Afterward the King looked so much like a giant bug that gulls nipped his ears, and pigeons pecked at him curiously.

The sun and moon rose and set thirty times. But the King was in the air all the while. He snatched sandwiches that his wife held out to him, and he slept flying on his side. But his legs got tangled with his sword, making it difficult for him to sleep.

Peramund made many flying trips across his kingdom, enjoying immensely the cheers of his loyal people. But at night he preferred to be near the tower above the courtyard.

## The Enchanted Spell Is Broken

All this time the King's soldiers were seeking the witch who had enchanted him. But she had gone off at the invitation of a mean old duke, to turn a prince whom he disliked into a croaking frog.

However, they were successful in seeking her out, and one bold soldier seized her firmly by her ear to prevent her escape. Then the soldiers dragged her to the palace.

They took her up into the tower and showed her King Peramund, who was still circling dizzily in the air.

Catching sight of the witch in the window, the King demanded that she disenchant him.

The witch said furiously, "Kings don't keep bargains. You can't deny that you've failed to keep yours."

"But, my good woman!" shouted the King vexedly. "I've no choice in the matter. I can't possibly grant your desire. You asked that I give my oldest daughter to a goblin. But as it happens, I don't even possess a daughter, only you went off in a huff before I could mention it."

"Oh!" said the witch, wrinkling her long, ugly nose. "I see! That makes quite a difference. So now I will disenchant you."

She muttered and mumbled some magic words, and immediately Peramund settled down as lightly as a feather upon the red clay bricks in the courtyard below.

After that the King had to learn to walk all over again, but he could never walk in a straight line. He had gone round and round the tower of the palace so many times that he was wound up, and he never again became completely unwound.

# Young Citizens
# of Other Lands

# At Home in Any Language

"I hope you will like Mexico City," said Mr. York as his family stepped from a taxicab in front of their new home. Mr. York was a highway engineer and had been in Mexico for weeks. His wife and son had just arrived.

"I'm sure we'll like it," said Mrs. York. "And as soon as we learn Spanish, we'll feel right at home."

Roy seemed doubtful, but he looked around with wondering eyes at the bright-colored houses, tall palm trees, and lovely blossoms.

"Flowers in January!" cried Roy, thinking of the snow back home in the United States.

"Here's the patio," said Mr. York, opening the gate into a sunny, walled-in garden. "It is like an outdoor living room."

When the baggage was unpacked, Mr. York went back to work. Roy, feeling lonely, got his baseball. Then picking up his bat and glove, he went out into the patio. Suddenly a baseball sailed over his head and struck a palm tree behind him. Roy looked around, trying to find the person who had thrown it, and saw a group of Mexican boys peering through the patio gate.

"They look scared," Roy thought. "Maybe they're afraid they broke something."

"Come in!" he called. When they failed to do so, Roy realized that the boys did not understand English.

Opening the gate, Roy beckoned to the boys. They understood this second invitation and came crowding into the patio, chattering excitedly in Spanish.

Roy's face lighted up. "Play ball," he cried, tossing the ball to a boy wearing a baseball glove. The boy caught it and just as promptly threw it back. Roy leaped up into the air and made the catch, while the Mexican boys yelled their approval.

When one boy motioned with his bat toward the park across the street, Roy did not hesitate. He got his cap, picked up his bat and glove, and ran out with them.

In the park more boys were waiting, and to Roy's astonishment, they had a real baseball diamond! Roy looked around. Counting himself, there were eighteen boys—exactly the right number for two teams. The captains chose their players, and the game began.

Roy did not understand any of the Spanish words the Mexican boys were using, but he understood baseball. That was enough.

When Roy's turn at bat came, he stepped to the plate. Then came the first pitch.

Roy swung and missed. He straightened the brim of his cap and gripped his bat.

Ssst! The second pitch whizzed by so fast that Roy didn't have time to get his bat off his shoulder. His teammates were yelling frantically and jumping up and down.

Two strikes! Roy had one more chance.

This time he was ready. Crack! The ball soared out into center field. Roy raced for first base and then kept on toward second. The center fielder tried for the ball, but it bounced off his glove. Roy rounded second, passed third, and with a burst of speed slid home. He had made a home run!

The boys whooped and yelled and threw their bats and gloves into the air.

When the game ended, Roy's team had lost 7 to 8. But he didn't mind losing a game, for he had won new friends. As they reached the gate, the boys separated, and Roy said, "So long, fellows. Thanks for the game."

"*Muchas gracias*," they all cried, and then they waved and called, "*Adios, adios*."

Roy had learned that *adios* means good-by and that *muchas gracias* is many thanks.

"*Adios*," Roy called to his new friends.

"*Mañana*," shouted the Mexican boys.

"*Mañana?*" Roy repeated in a puzzled tone. Then he saw his father coming down the avenue. "Oh, Dad," he cried, "will you tell me what *mañana* means?"

"Tomorrow," answered his father, smiling.

"But I'd like to know now," begged Roy.

Mr. York laughed. "*Mañana* is the Spanish word for tomorrow," he explained.

"That means a game tomorrow," Roy cried. Then he reported the day's happenings.

"How could you feel so much at home with the Mexican boys when you don't understand their language?" his father asked.

"Oh," said Roy. "We all understood baseball. That's the same in any language."

# The Red-Brimmed Hat

## Tomas Disappears

Slowly across the street, in the noonday sun came Pedro, carrying his brother Tomas on his back. Reaching the stall that his mother had sent him to tend in the market square, he set the baby down on a rug.

"How can I wait on customers and keep you out of mischief?" Pedro asked, as he began to straighten up the rugs and blankets.

Tomas meantime was crawling away as fast as he could. When Pedro finally caught the baby, he put a rope around his fat waist and tied him to a table leg. "Now, I won't need to watch you," said Pedro, giving Tomas a squeeze, for he wasn't really angry.

Tomas clapped his chubby hands. Perhaps being tied up was some new kind of game.

"There!" said Pedro, kneeling to put a rug under the table. "You sit on this rug, out of the sun, and here is a gourd to play with." He chose an orange-colored gourd from a willow basket. Tomas chuckled as he took it.

Pedro yawned. Leaning against a palm tree he said to himself, "The customers are now taking a *siesta*. I shall take a *siesta*, too." He closed his eyes, and soon he slept.

Suddenly he awoke to find his mother shaking him roughly. "What did you do with Tomas, idle one?" she cried. "I did not send you here to take a *siesta*."

Pedro rubbed his eyes and peered under the table. The rug was there, but Tomas was nowhere in sight. The rope was gone, and so was the gourd. Fear gripped Pedro.

"I—I don't know," he said. "He was here a short time ago. I tied him to the table, but he is gone. So are the rope and the gourd."

"Where is Tomas now?" cried his terrified mother, weeping. "Have you let some thief come and steal him?"

"Please, *mama*," said Pedro, "do not weep."

By this time a curious crowd had gathered at the stall. News travels fast in an open square, and so the disappearance of Tomas had caused a great commotion in the plaza.

One old woman said, "Perhaps the basketmaker who set up his stall on the other side of Pedro took the child. He left very early." Then she added with a shrug, "No, no, I do not say that the basketmaker did steal him."

Pedro asked questions, but no one could report much about the basketmaker. Some thought that he had come from a mountain village to the north. He had a burro—they were certain of that. And his helper was a tall, dark-faced boy whom no one knew. Perhaps this boy was the thief who had taken Tomas. Pedro must try to find the boy.

Turning to his mother, Pedro said, "I'll ride my burro along the north road and ask if anyone has seen little Tomas. Someone may remember seeing his red-brimmed hat." Then Pedro started slowly across the plaza.

"Hurry, idle one," called his mother, "and catch the thief who took my blessed baby."

Halfway across the plaza Pedro saw his friend Carlota standing on the steps of the village church. She beckoned to him.

"Is it true that Tomas has disappeared?" she cried. "Can I be of help?"

"I am riding out to look for him," answered Pedro. "Ride with me up the mountain. We may find the thief who took Tomas." Then Pedro told about the basketmaker, and the two children hurried to Pedro's home.

"Come, Rosa," said Pedro, putting a rug on the little burro's back. Then the children climbed on and jogged out of the village on the path that went north.

### Rosa Makes a Discovery

The path wound up the mountainside like a narrow ribbon. Sometimes it dipped into the valley. Occasionally it wound to the top of a peak. Then Pedro and Carlota could look down and see the little farms spread out like neat squares on the valley floor below them.

Only the tapping of Rosa's nimble hoofs and the occasional chirping of the crickets disturbed the silence of the mountainside as the children jogged up the narrow path.

After winding through tall pine trees the path finally grew very steep. First Carlota and then Pedro slid off Rosa's back. So the children led Rosa up the path to where the trail was not so steep. Then they mounted her once more and jogged slowly on. All of a sudden the burro stopped with a jolt.

"What is it?" cried Carlota as she peered anxiously about. "Did she step into a rut?"

"Perhaps she picked up a stone," said Pedro as he got down to examine Rosa's hoofs.

But Rosa had not picked up a stone, nor had she stepped into a rut. She had seen something beside the path. There at the foot of a tall cactus lay the red-brimmed hat! But where was the baby? What had happened to chubby little Tomas?

"Pedro," wept Carlota, "what can we do?"

"Come," said Pedro, trying to hide his fear. "We must turn back to get help. Who can tell what kind of people these may be who would steal a baby like Tomas?"

"Go just a little farther, Pedro," coaxed Carlota as she stooped to pick up the hat. "Maybe we can find Tomas all by ourselves."

"Come, then," said Pedro, and the two again got on Rosa's back. Carlota gripped the hat tightly as they jogged up the trail.

By and by Rosa stopped and pricked up her ears as though she had heard something on the peak above. Pedro and Carlota listened intently but could hear nothing.

"Go on, Rosa," Pedro said sternly. "We have not yet reached the top." But Rosa just gave a hee-haw and planted her feet firmly.

"There's no moving her now," said Pedro with a shrug. "She has a bad temper."

"Listen," whispered Carlota as the faint sound of footsteps came to her ears.

"That is what disturbed Rosa," said Pedro. "If it is the thief who took Tomas, he will be a tall, dark-faced boy."

As they stood by a tall cactus waiting, the sound of footsteps came nearer. Presently a boy bounded nimbly down the path, with a large basket strapped on his back.

It was Carlota who whispered, "It is the same boy who had the stall next to your mother's. Speak to him, Pedro. You must find out if he has seen Tomas."

### The Search Is Ended

The boy did not notice the children until
Pedro cleared his throat and spoke.

"Please," Pedro began hopefully, "have
you seen anything of a chubby little boy—
just a baby—in a red-brimmed hat?"

"Why?" demanded the boy sternly, as he
stooped to ease a strap that held the basket.

"Pedro's baby brother disappeared today," answered Carlota. "We found his hat by a cactus down where the road turns. And you were near him when he disappeared. Your stall was next to the stall of Pedro's mother."

The boy gave a shrug and said, "Yes, I saw the baby and his red-brimmed hat. But I did not see him go away—nor did I see anyone take him."

"Then we must go back without him!" cried Pedro, turning away to conceal his grief.

"Wait," ordered the boy. He loosened the strap and swung the big basket down from his shoulders. Then he beckoned, and the two wondering children stooped to look inside.

Nestled at the bottom of the basket, Tomas lay fast asleep!

Carlota reached down and picked up Tomas, who was beginning to wake up.

Pedro's grief had now vanished. "Bless you!" he cried, embracing the baby. Then he turned once more to the tall stranger.

"What were you going to do with Tomas?" he asked, looking intently at the tall boy.

"Return him to his home," said the boy.

Then Pedro's temper rose. "Why did you steal him in the first place?" he asked.

"I didn't steal him," the boy said. "When we reached home, up near the mountain peak, we found him in one of our baskets. He must have loosened his rope and crawled in when someone was taking a siesta."

Pedro realized that the boy was accusing him, and he knew he deserved a scolding, yet he asked, "Why didn't you say at once that you had Tomas? Why did you conceal him?"

The boy laughed. "Did you think I would give him to the first person who came along? I wanted to be sure he belonged to you."

Now that the disappearance of Tomas was explained, Pedro thanked the boy warmly. "What do you call yourself?" he added.

"I call myself Pablo," the boy answered promptly. "If you please," he continued, "I'll carry the baby down the mountain to where the path isn't so steep. You might drop him."

"Many thanks," said Pedro. "I'm sorry that I accused you of taking Tomas." Then he put the child back into the basket.

Tomas stood up, and his chubby face was covered with smiles as Pablo bounded down the steep mountain path.

On the way back Pedro and Carlota laughed at the jolting of the burro and the ruts in the path, for all their grief had vanished.

At last they reached a clearing, and Pablo gazed down on the village nestling in the valley. "Good-by," said Pablo, easing the basket down from his back.

"Good-by, Pablo," answered Pedro, and he embraced him warmly. "Bless you for finding Tomas."

"Let us meet in the plaza near the church next market day," suggested Carlota. And Tomas smiled from under his red-brimmed hat as Pablo disappeared up the path.

## Adventure in Guatemala

### A Shopping Trip

Tommy and Pete slept late on their first morning in Guatemala. The strong sunlight, pouring in at the window, did not waken them. Neither did the ringing of the bells in the little whitewashed church.

But when a brilliantly colored peacock, sitting on a wall opposite the window, began to shriek, they awoke with a start. Then both boys sat upright in bed, staring.

The boys had arrived late the day before, from their home in the United States, to visit Cousin Sylvia's plantation home in Guatemala. And now for the first time they began to realize that they were in a very different country.

"It's a peacock!" cried Pete, rubbing his eyes in amazement. He could hardly believe that he wasn't still asleep and dreaming.

"Oh, what a gorgeous tail!" cried Tommy. The peacock stretched his glossy neck and shrieked again. Then he jumped down to strut about the patio, unfolding his tail in a fan of brilliant gold and blue feathers.

"Oh," said Pete, "look at him strut. I'd like to touch him to see if he is real."

Looking into the garden he saw graceful palms, brilliant blossoms, and lacy, trailing vines. Throngs of birds filled the air. "Is this just a magnificent dream," Pete asked slowly, "or is that a real banana tree out there?"

"I guess nearly anything can be real in Guatemala," said Tommy, leaning out to look.

Sylvia came skipping into the patio just in time to hear the boys' remarks about her beautiful country. She decided right then that she was going to like her cousins from the United States very much indeed.

"Hurry up and get dressed," Sylvia called. "We are going to the store to get your new hats—sombreros we call them."

After breakfast the children strolled down an avenue of palms to the plantation store.

Old Pedro, the storekeeper, spoke softly in Spanish as the children entered.

"He asks what we want," Sylvia explained. "Pedro understands English, but he always speaks Spanish. I am very fond of Pedro."

Then she turned and spoke to the old man. "Please, Pedro, two big sombreros for my cousins from the United States."

Pedro took down from the shelf a pile of peaked, wide-brimmed hats. Tommy selected a sombrero with a band of white and green. Pete chose one with a brilliant red band.

With their new hats on their heads the boys strutted out of the store.

"*Muchas gracias*," said Pedro as they left.

"*Adios*," answered Sylvia, starting out the door just as a squeaking cart, drawn by black-and-white oxen, drew near the store.

"May we ride?" she asked the wrinkled old man in the cart. At his nod, Sylvia and the boys got in and jolted down the long avenue.

As soon as the three children reached the house, they showed the sombreros to Sylvia's mother. Then they set out to see the banana trees and coffee groves. Sylvia, carrying a riding whip in her hand, walked ahead with the dogs, Roger and Friar.

"I carry this whip because other big dogs sometimes fight with Friar," she explained. "They behave if I just wave it in the air."

## An Amazing Plantation

The children walked up a dusty lane and strolled along between rows of banana trees and glossy green coffee bushes that were heavy with red berries.

Whole families of workers were carefully twisting off the coffee berries and dropping them into baskets hung about their waists.

"I never knew coffee was red," said Pete. "All the coffee I've ever seen was brown."

"The coffee beans are inside the berries," said Sylvia, as she selected one and broke it apart. Inside were two gray-white beans, shaped like half-moons, facing each other.

"Those gray-white beans don't look very much like coffee either," said Tommy.

"Well, many things are done before you'd know they are coffee," replied Sylvia. "Big machines take off the red outside covering. Then the gray coffee beans are carefully dried.

233

"Next the beans are shipped to the United States, where the coffee is roasted. Then it looks like the coffee you see in the stores."

Sylvia and the boys loitered along a shady lane, near rows of tiny whitewashed houses, each with a banana tree growing in the yard. Here the plantation workers lived. By one house a kind-faced woman knelt, kneading a piece of dough with her hands. Beside the doorway hung strings of bright peppers and curiously shaped gourds. Inside the house a fire burned on the dirt floor.

"What is she making?" asked Tommy as the children drew closer.

"We call them *tortillas*," Sylvia answered. "*Tortillas* take the place of bread with us."

The woman kneaded the soft dough in the palms of her hands until it was round and as thin as paper. Then she went in and placed a flat, clay bowl on the fire, and in it she laid the thin pancakes of kneaded dough. As soon as they were cooked, the woman carefully lifted them from the fire.

"*Tortillas?*" she asked as she held them out to the children.

"*Muchas gracias*," said Sylvia, thanking her in Spanish.

"I like *tortillas*," said Tommy, finishing his in a few hasty bites.

"Mm-mm, so do I," echoed Pete.

"I'm glad you do, because we eat lots of them here on the plantation," Sylvia said to him.

As they turned to go, the woman smiled. "*Adios*," she said. And she again picked up some dough and commenced to knead it.

The three children wandered on, passing little whitewashed plantation church th stood in a large grove of palm trees. A almost every turn of the lane Tommy and Pe made some new discovery—a curious animal, an interesting-looking fruit, or a fragrant blossom. The plantation was truly amazing to Sylvia's North American cousins.

The lane finally ended, and Sylvia and the boys found themselves in thick, jungle-like forest.

Here they loitered awhile, almost lost in the jungle ferns. Finally they crossed a stream and entered the woods on the opposite side.

These fragrant, jungly woods were full of lacy-leafed ferns and glossy, trailing vines. Gorgeous jungle flowers blossomed thickly. Brilliantly colored birds flew here and there, and chattering monkeys sat in the branches above their heads.

Soon they came to a clearing, and Sylvia cried out, "Oh, I smell *panela!*"

"What's *panela?*" Pete asked.

"*Panela* is brown sugar," Sylvia answered.

The children ran and soon came to a row of square huts set in a grove of palm trees. The tempting smell of freshly made *panela* came from a shed at the end of the village, where sugar was being made.

A short distance from the shed a mother pig lay in the middle of the dusty path with her squealing family. Sylvia and the boys knew that a mother pig sometimes has a bad temper. So they made a detour around her. Hearing the pig grunt, they turned quickly. There, near the pig, crawled a baby.

At that moment Friar tore from behind a hut. Seeing the mother pig lying directly in his path, he stopped and began to growl.

Sylvia was terrified.

"Come here, Friar," she said sternly, while Pete gripped Roger's collar with both hands.

But Friar kept on growling. Occasionally he would bark furiously. Then finally the enraged pig arose and started toward the dog, squealing madly.

Sylvia added to the commotion by screaming, "The baby! The baby!" For the child was directly between Friar and the pig.

Tommy, realizing the child's danger, darted forward, picked up the baby, and raced behind the hut.

At the same time Pete snatched the riding whip out of Sylvia's hand. He beat off the enraged pig and shouted at the dogs to keep them away. Sylvia and Tommy grasped Roger and Friar by their collars. They held on to them until the mother pig gave a snort and turned back to her squealing babies.

The danger was past.

"Friar, I'll never risk taking you with me again. Someone might have been hurt," cried Sylvia. Then she gave Roger a pat.

Turning to Pete and Tommy, Sylvia said, "You were both splendid, and you deserve a reward. You shall have some extra *panela*. It tastes just like candy."

# A South American Visit

When Mr. Hollyberry had to take a trip to South America, he took Mrs. Hollyberry and Jane and Tommy with him. It was thrilling for the two children to travel in the big airplane that carried them swiftly from one new place to another.

Jane and Tommy had heard so much about Buenos Aires, beautiful city of Argentina, that they were very happy when they finally reached the city late one evening.

"Is Buenos Aires as big as New York City?" Tommy inquired the next morning as he stood admiring a park opposite the hotel.

"No," answered Mr. Hollyberry. "But it is the largest city in South America."

Right after lunch the children and their
mother went shopping in the main business
center of Buenos Aires. No automobiles or
buses are allowed here, and people stroll in
the middle of the avenue. This traffic rule
surprised Jane and Tommy very much.

"Oh!" said Jane, looking in a shop window.
"See the red school bag! May I buy it?"

"Why, yes," said Mrs. Hollyberry. "That
should be a very nice gift to take home from
South America."

Tommy was so intent upon a toy monkey
in the next window that he did not see them
go into the shop.

When Tommy looked around, Jane and his mother had gone. He lingered along the wide avenue, hoping to find them, but soon he was hopelessly lost in a throng of shoppers. He looked for a policeman to ask for help, but he could not locate one. By this time he was on an unfamiliar street near a park.

Some school children were standing on the edge of the sidewalk, waiting to cross the avenue. They seemed to be waiting for a policeman's signal. But where was the officer?

Then Tommy saw a man in a white uniform standing in a traffic tower that had ferns planted at its base. Above the traffic officer's head was an umbrella. At a signal from him the waiting children crossed the avenue.

So Tommy went over and stood beside the traffic tower. Looking up he called out, "My name is Tommy Hollyberry. I am lost."

The policeman did not seem to hear him.

"I AM TOMMY HOLLYBERRY. I AM LOST. WHERE IS THE CITY HOTEL, PLEASE?"

Still the policeman looked straight ahead. But Tommy kept on. This time he stood on tiptoe and shouted, "MY NAME IS——"

"May I help you?" asked a boy nearby.

"Yes," answered Tommy. "I'm lost."

The boy then spoke to the policeman in Spanish. "The North American boy is lost."

Looking down from the tower the policeman asked something in Spanish.

The boy spoke in English to Tommy. "The officer asks where you live," he said.

"I am staying at the City Hotel," Tommy answered promptly.

"I know where the City Hotel is," Tommy's new friend told him. "Allow me to take you there." Then the South American boy introduced himself. "My name is Carlos," he said. "Come with me."

The boys took time to get acquainted on the way back to the hotel. But they forgot that Tommy's parents would be distressed on account of his being absent so long.

"Oh, Tommy," cried his mother when he and Carlos arrived. "What happened?"

"I was lost," said Tommy. "But my friend Carlos brought me home."

Mrs. Hollyberry said, "Thank you, Carlos."

Carlos bowed. "Then may I be permitted to show you Buenos Aires? Would you like to see the Pink House, where our President lives?"

"The Pink House!" Jane broke in. "Oh, I'd love to see it. Our President lives in the White House."

When Carlos had left, Tommy reported how his meeting with Carlos had happened, and Jane proudly showed him her new red school bag. "I wish we could speak Spanish as well as Carlos speaks English," she said.

"Perhaps you should get a Spanish Reader to put in that new school bag of yours when you start to school next fall," suggested Tommy with a smile.

# Mario's Pet

### A Capture

It was Mario's turn to take the goats to graze high in the grassy hills of Argentina. The damp cold of early dawn still lingered in the valley as he rode the brown-and-white pinto out from his father's farm.

The goats bounded nimbly along the path, kicking their heels and shaking their long, curved horns. Mario yawned as the pinto followed the goats idly across the level floor of the valley and along a path that wound for miles among the hills.

By midmorning the sun had climbed high, and soon the hot wind licked at Mario like a flame. Finally the pinto halted and hung its head wearily. Mario straightened in his saddle. Just beyond stood a little thorn tree that would protect them from the hot sun.

"Come, lazy one," Mario said to the pinto. "Here we rest. I feel drowsy."

Mario found a level spot beneath the thorn tree and ate the corn cakes he had in his pocket. Then he lay down and went to sleep.

The pinto nibbled grass nearby, and the goats ambled down the hill. Even the noise of the crickets ceased. It was so still that a lizard slithered out from under a bush.

For a moment the lizard stared at Mario. Then it slithered unnoticed across his bare brown leg and vanished in the grass.

But there the lizard met trouble, for the black eyes of a large gray bird had spied it. The chuna darted at the lizard and tossed it against the ground several times before he swallowed it.

Then the long-legged bird picked up a tiny pebble in his sharp bill and looked about for a target. Throwing a pebble is as easy for a chuna as pitching a ball is for a boy.

The chuna looked intently at the tree for a moment and then drew back his long neck. The next instant the bird's neck shot forward, and the pebble flew to its mark.

Ping! As the pebble struck the tree, the chuna lifted its head, and the gray feathers on its long, bony neck stood up proudly. The chuna did not linger but started off swiftly.

Mario sat up beneath the thorn tree and rubbed his leg where the pebble, bouncing off the tree, had hit him. He stumbled to his feet and looked about drowsily. "Now what could have hit me? *Ahi*, I see a chuna. It must have thrown this pebble."

Mario took from his saddle a boleadora, the homemade weapon which he always had with him when he went into the hills. For he never knew when he might see a bird that he could capture with his boleadora and take home alive for a pet.

The weapon was simple. It was just three leather-covered balls, two of wood and one of stone, hung from three cowhide thongs.

Spying the chuna running through the brush, Mario moved cautiously forward. He would throw the boleadora at the chuna's feet and tangle them in the tough cowhide thongs so that the bird could not get away. Then he would capture it.

Mario grasped the boleadora firmly by one of the three round balls that hung from the tough thongs. He swung it several times above his head. Then he let it fly. There was a loud noise—half squawk, half bark— and the bird dropped in the bushes. Mario quickly captured his prize.

"I'm glad you are a young bird," Mario said happily. "You'll make a splendid pet. I shall wrap the thongs about your feet, and you cannot break loose. Then I shall carry you home nestled in my arms. So!"

All that long afternoon while the goats grazed, Mario's thoughts were on the bird he had captured. At last he had a pet!

His father owned the pinto, and Jorge, his older brother, owned a dog. His mother had her parrot. Once he had tamed a kid, but as soon as the kid was a full-grown goat, his father had sold it. After that Mario had not made a pet of any of the kids.

On the way home Mario loitered along the road, talking to his chuna. "Perhaps I can teach you to throw stones at targets. *Ahi*, but you shall be the very cleverest bird in Argentina. Everyone shall envy me."

### Tiro's Lesson

Mario named his pet Tiro, which in Spanish means a throw or a shot. In a few days the bird acted as if he owned the farm on which Mario lived. He kept it free from mice and lizards, but he got into mischief, too.

Tiro apparently liked nothing better than to start a commotion among the animals.

He threw pebbles at the goats and nipped the tiny ears of the kids. He never ceased to worry and disturb the parrot. That bird did not like the chuna, and she shrieked at him whenever he came near. If Tiro picked up a stone, however, the parrot soon hid.

January, which is midsummer in Argentina, came to a close. The creek was almost dry. And in the corn patch the ears of corn grew large and fat. Occasionally the blackbirds swarmed in from the hills and ate the corn, causing much damage to the crop.

"Mario," said Jorge one morning, "why is it that you have not tried your boleadora on the robber blackbirds? That pumpkin-headed scarecrow we put up does not frighten them."

Mario's mother looked at them and spoke sternly. "We shall have no corn to dry for the winter if the blackbirds keep on eating. Today Mario must stay in the corn patch and drive the robber birds off. Jorge will take the goats to graze."

Jorge grinned. "I do not envy you the job," he said teasingly to Mario. "I am not sorry to be absent from the hot corn patch today."

Mario walked slowly toward the cornfield where the scarecrow stood. A strong breeze stirred the dust into little whirlwinds—the witches' midsummer dance, Mario called it. The chuna darted ahead of him, but the blackbirds did not move from the corn patch until Mario pitched a pebble at the scarecrow.

When the birds swarmed back, Mario got ready to pitch another pebble. But just then Tiro threw a stone that struck the scarecrow's hat with a loud ping, and the birds rustled noisily out of the corn patch.

Mario wiggled his bare toes in the dust. Maybe he could teach the chuna to use the scarecrow's hat for a target. Then he could sleep while Tiro kept the robber birds away.

"Look, Tiro," called Mario as he pitched a pebble at the scarecrow. Then Tiro threw a pebble. Again and again they practiced. Finally Mario lay down with his hat over his eyes. In just a moment—ping! His hat bounced off. Mario sat up and said to Tiro, "The scarecrow is your target, not I."

Tiro's eyes twinkled, and his long neck curved like a question mark.

Again the birds rustled in the corn. Tiro picked up a pebble. Ping! The birds left.

"Good, Tiro!" laughed Mario. "Now you can chase off the robber birds while I rest."

Mario yawned and lay down again, but this time he tucked his hat under him and left the corn patch to Tiro.

# Christmas in Alaska

## A Disappointment

Roy York waved gaily to his father and ran down a snowy path leading from the Alaskan town that had been his home for months. He was on his way to the Eskimo tent village to meet Tana, for the two boys had promised to get a Christmas tree for the school party.

"I'm glad Dad is a highway engineer," Roy said to himself. "Last winter we were in Mexico, and now—Alaska."

Just as Roy reached the tent where Tana lived, Tana's mother opened the tent flap. Roy could see a kettle of reindeer milk standing on the smoky fire inside.

"Tana," she called, "Roy is ready to go up in the hills and get the Christmas tree."

Tana came out of the tent to greet Roy as Tana's mother continued, "How is it, Roy, that you can pop kernels of corn so that a hard kernel blossoms to many times its size? The teacher's invitation says that I will see that on Monday at the Christmas party."

Before Roy could explain, the voice of Tana's father came from behind the tent. "Why is there talk of a Christmas party? We will not be within snowshoe distance of this village on Christmas. The reindeer have now eaten all the moss in this area, and we dare not linger here."

Tana and Roy could not believe their ears. What about all their wonderful plans for the Christmas party only two days away?

Just then Tana's old grandfather spoke up, "We depend on our reindeer for our food, our clothing, and our tents. Fierce storms now threaten all this part of Alaska, and the Eskimos must take the herds to a sheltered place where they can find food."

"Yes, we move at once," said Tana's father.

"Father," Tana cried, greatly distressed, "we promised Miss White! Without the fir tree she can't have a Christmas party at the schoolhouse. We promised her a tree."

Tana's father and the older man looked at each other. When the grandfather nodded, Tana's father said, "Go, then, for I have always said you must keep a promise. Next time don't give your word until you have asked permission. When you come back, we must leave. We will be far away by Monday."

Tana's mother now spoke again. "I am glad you are permitted to go for the tree," she said, giving the boys a slice of cheese apiece. "Take this to eat when you get hungry." Then she added sadly, "I wish we could stay for the Christmas party, and then we could see those popped kernels."

The boys thanked her. Tana, grasping a handful of moss to tempt his pet reindeer, walked out toward the herd.

"Cloot!" he said softly. At the sound of Tana's voice the reindeer bolted to the far side of the herd, for he apparently did not like to be harnessed to the sled.

## A Wild Ride

The patient reindeer stood chewing their
cuds as Tana made his way carefully through
the herd, moss in hand.  Meanwhile Roy was
waiting beside the sled, impatient to be off.

Catching sight of Cloot in the herd Tana
tried to silence the sound of his boots as he
crept up on his pet and offered the moss.
Just as Cloot reached for the moss, Tana
tossed a strap over his head.

He held the reindeer while Roy brought the
sled and harnessed Cloot to it.  Quickly the
boys jumped on the sled.  Tana gripped the
rein, and Cloot started off, jogging along
the frozen creek.

The rays of the sun, shining on the snow, almost blinded the boys. So they put on eye shades with narrow openings in them.

Cloot jogged along with a stiff-legged trot, and by midmorning he had reached the hills where the finest fir trees grew.

Tana pulled on the rein, attempting to halt his steed. But Cloot made a wide curve and bolted off through the woods at breakneck speed, jolting the sled over frozen ruts.

Roy tried dragging his feet in the snow to make Cloot slow down. But this only made the desperate reindeer leap ahead faster. The boys were wondering what they were going to do, when Cloot suddenly halted. The sled jolted the boys, who lost their balance and pitched headlong into the snow. Over and over they rolled.

Cloot, meantime, stood pawing the snow and eagerly munching moss and twigs.

"Cloot has located food!" cried Tana.

"He discovered something else, too," Roy shouted, pointing to a beautiful fir tree.

As the boys set to work cutting down their fir, Roy said, "Now maybe you won't have to leave before Christmas, Tana. If Cloot has found food for himself here, perhaps there is enough in this area for all the herd."

"I hope so," answered the Eskimo boy, his eyes dancing. "Now maybe Mother will see the kernels pop into beautiful blossoms."

When the tree was cut, the boys rolled it in the reindeer skins they had brought to keep the branches from scraping on the ground and being damaged. When the boys lashed it to the sled, Cloot, who was watching their every movement, snorted with alarm.

"Quiet, Cloot, quiet!" said Roy, grasping the sled to steady the animal.

But Cloot did not heed, for no sooner had Tana gripped the reins than the restless steed turned his head and saw what seemed to be a strange monster added to his load.

The startled reindeer bolted suddenly and set out at a terrific gallop. There was no stopping him! Tana lost his balance, fell off the sled, and was dragged along by the rein that was wrapped around his hand. He barely escaped being trampled by the hoofs of the bounding reindeer. But he managed to clamber back on the sled beside his terrified companion.

As Cloot swept on through the snowy woods, the sky became dark and threatening. Soon it might commence to storm, for even now the frozen flakes were beginning to lash the boys' faces. If a wild blizzard should strike, they might even freeze. The two were so terrified that neither spoke a word.

Suddenly Cloot turned. It was impossible for the boys to see in the blinding swirl of snowflakes, and they had no idea where the runaway deer was taking them. They clung to each other desperately, as the rocking movement of the sled made them dizzy.

On they went. Would Cloot never tire?

But suddenly the sled struck a stump and gave a terrific jolt. Their wild ride was over!

## Cloot Saves the Day

Jumping off the sled the two boys looked around and were amazed to find themselves right back where they had started.

Cloot had brought them home!

"Oh, I should have known," laughed Tana, "that a reindeer always wants to be with the herd when a blizzard strikes."

"That is so," said his father, as he and the grandfather stood laughing at the boys.

"Father!" Tana shouted. "Cloot ran away, but he found green moss and twigs nearby. So his good act balances the bad one."

"You'll be here for Christmas!" Roy cried.

Just at that moment Tana's mother heard the commotion and came out of the tent. Roy and Tana had to tell the news of their good fortune all over again.

"Then all is well," said Tana's grandfather, smiling at Tana and his eager companion.

Tana's mother, standing by the open tent flap, laughed aloud with pleasure. "Now we shall see how the corn kernels open into dainty white blossoms," she said. "And we can help trim the tree for the school party."

"Yes," said Roy, smiling at his Eskimo friends. "All the time we were up in the woods, I was hoping that Tana and all of you would be here for the Christmas holidays."

"Cloot really deserves a special Christmas present for locating the moss," said Tana. He unhitched the panting steed, and just as soon as Cloot was free, he gave a snort and jogged off to join the herd.

"There'll be a commotion when he tells the news to his companions," laughed Roy.

Tana turned to his father standing nearby and said, "Thank you, Father, for allowing us to keep our promise to get the tree. If you hadn't, Cloot never would have found the fresh moss close to our village, and we would not have been here for Christmas!"

"It always pays to keep a promise," his grandfather reminded him quietly.

# The Great Outdoors

# A Camp in the Canyon

### Finding a Camp Site

From the minute they had seen the clearing, the Lane family knew they had found a perfect site for a camp. Thick pine forests grew on either side of the clearing, and beyond them rose the walls of the canyon.

While Mother was starting supper, Father split wood for the fire. Jill went after a pail of water, and Terry built a rock stove on a sandy place not far from the tent.

"Look at the waterfall!" called Jill as she came back with her brimming pail of water.

Terry glanced up and caught the gleam of distant water tumbling over the canyon's rim. The lingering rays of the setting sun made the water sparkle like brilliant jewels.

"What a view!" he exclaimed. "I want to explore this canyon from end to end."

"Let's have supper first," Mother called.

"Yes!" said Father, hurrying to help her. "I'm as hungry as a bear."

While Terry was busy with the fire, he heard a sharp voice call, "Say, there!"

Terry looked around and saw a boy about his own age carrying a trout rod over his shoulder. He was frowning at the fire.

"Hello," said Terry in a friendly tone.

The boy pointed his trout rod at the fire. "Put that out," he demanded sternly. "You can't build fires here."

His tone made Terry just a little angry. "Who are you?" he asked.

"I'm Lewis Drake," the boy said. "This is my dad's land. He won't permit campers."

Hearing the boys, Mr. Lane came forward. "Hello," he said, "what's the trouble?"

"Campers aren't allowed in this canyon," repeated Lewis. "Campers start forest fires."

"Well, we are always very careful about fires," Mr. Lane replied with a smile. "We have built this rock stove in the open, and we never go off and leave a fire burning. If you tell your father that, maybe he'll consent to our camping here for a few days."

"Dad isn't home," answered the boy in the same unfriendly tone as before.

"Very well," Mr. Lane said slowly. "We'll move on and find another camp site."

The boy walked away, and the Lanes soon put out the fire, packed their things, and left in search of another site.

"There are plenty of good places to camp," Father said. "We'll find one soon."

Fortunately they found one before dark on a ranch farther up the canyon. "We'll ask permission before we pitch our tent," Father said as he drove to the ranch house.

Much to the family's relief, the rancher gave his consent readily. "I think I can recognize good campers when I see them," he said. "You don't look like careless folks who'd leave fires to destroy the timber."

The Lanes promised that they would be careful, and soon they were settled on the new camp site. Terry and Jill did not like it as well as the first place, but at least they knew that they were welcome.

The moon had risen before they finished eating supper, and the peaceful quiet of the midsummer night was broken only by the faint chirping of the crickets.

## Exploring the Canyon

The new camp site proved very exciting. Father, with fishing rod in hand, cast for trout in the streams, and Jill made good use of her camera as they all explored the canyon.

Terry discovered a deserted shack in which pack rats had hidden their stolen treasures—a gold buckle, brass pins, and other shiny objects. Once they startled a dainty fawn sleeping on a bed of lacy ferns near the falls, and bluejays scolded them noisily.

One morning Terry and Jill visited the ranger station up on the rim of the canyon. Dick Allen, the ranger who was on lookout duty, took them to the top of the fire tower and let them look through his field glasses at the vast timber region below.

Distant objects seemed close through the powerful glasses, and the ranger explained how field glasses and airplanes helped the rangers patrol that vast region.

"A fire patrol is always on duty," he said. "Our timber must not be destroyed."

"Don't you ever get lonesome?" Jill asked, looking out over the pine wilderness that seemed to meet the western sky.

"We haven't much time to get lonesome," answered Dick Allen with a smile. "We're far too busy. Even with the help of planes, patrolling this wilderness is quite a job."

As Jill and Terry thanked him and started home, the ranger added, "I know you'll help us prevent fires. Remember, one careless act might destroy this whole forest."

## Fighting a Fire

Halfway down from the rim of the canyon Terry stooped over to tie his boot laces. "I smell something burning!" he exclaimed.

They hurried along, looking on every side for a blaze or a curl of smoke. Finally they discovered a patch of burning moss.

"Get some water! Quick!" Terry said.

The brook was only a few steps away, but they had nothing that would hold water, not even a cap.

"Oh, look!" Jill cried in alarm as a patch of dry pine needles burst into flames.

"I'll stamp the fire out. My boots are heavy," cried Terry, trampling on the burning moss and needles. Jill tried to help, but the crackling flames scorched her boots.

The two were so intent on their task that they did not see Lewis Drake running up the canyon with his trout rod until a dry twig snapped beneath his feet.

"Hi!" Terry yelled. "Come and help us put this fire out."

Lewis put down his trout rod. "So you *did* start a fire!" he said accusingly.

"We didn't start it," Jill denied.

"Well," said Lewis, "whether you did or not, it's our job to put it out." Pulling off his sweater, he soaked it in the brook and handed it to Jill. "Beat the flames with it," he said. "We boys can use our shirts."

Both boys peeled off their shirts, and for a time all three fought the fire frantically.

"It's no use," Lewis said, throwing down his shirt. "We can't stop it. I wish I had a spade, so I could dig a ditch around the fire. A lot of this timber will be burned unless the fire patrol gets here soon."

"I'll go and get Dad," said Jill. "He'll know what to do."

"Good," cried Terry. "Lewis and I will keep working. But hurry!"

"Tell him to bring a spade," Lewis shouted as Jill sped down the path toward the camp.

Barely twenty minutes later Jill and her father returned, bringing Mr. Drake and other ranchers. By this time the forest rangers patrolling the region had sighted the fire and had arrived to direct the work.

Leaving Jill at a safe distance, Mr. Lane took his spade and joined the rangers who were digging a ditch to prevent the fire from spreading. Two rangers were slashing away the brushwood that was catching fire from the flying sparks. Others were beating the blazing grass with wet sacks they had soaked in the brook.

Pausing for a moment to wipe off his moist forehead, Mr. Lane caught sight of Terry and Lewis working together like old friends.

A wind began fanning the fire southward, and for three long hours the men fought on, their faces scorched and blackened by the heat and smoke. Suddenly it commenced to rain. A light sprinkle increased to a steady downpour that soaked the entire canyon.

"The timber's safe!" shouted a ranger, and the men ceased work in weary relief.

Pulling off his scorched gloves, Mr. Drake held out his hand to Mr. Lane. "Thanks for your help," he said. "If all campers were like your family, I'd put up signs saying *Welcome*, instead of *Keep Out*. After this you may camp on my land any time."

273

# Bushy Tail's Escape

One by one the pale stars came out in the summer sky above the forest. The night was filled with mysterious rustlings as throngs of small woodland creatures—mice, wood rats, and flying squirrels—ventured cautiously out from their hiding places.

They were risking their lives in search of food, and many of the weaker ones would not survive this adventure of the night.

Silent-winged owls kept watch in the dark branches of the trees, ready to pounce on any mouse or wood rat that dared to venture forth. Weasels and foxes prowled the forest trails, preying on weaker animals that were unable to defend themselves.

Hidden underground in their den, a father and mother chipmunk and their babies— even Bushy Tail, the frisky one—were sound asleep. All was peaceful in the den under an old stump.

Now and then sounds from the forest above came faintly into the burrow, causing the old chipmunks to stir uneasily in their sleep.

The doorway of the burrow was small, and the tunnel leading to their den was long and narrow. So the chipmunks had little to dread from most night prowlers.

But one prowler from which chipmunks are never safe is the weasel. His body is so slim that he can squeeze his way into the deepest part of a chipmunk's burrow. His sharp eyes can see the slightest movement in the grass, and his nose is as keen as the nose of a fox.

Tonight, while the chipmunks were quietly sleeping, a weasel was slyly making his way toward their burrow.

Presently Father Chipmunk awoke. Something warned him of danger, and he started up the tunnel at once.

In an instant the old chipmunk was at the burrow door. Here he paused and listened intently, but he heard no sound, and at first he saw nothing alarming.

Then suddenly on the dim hillside below him Father Chipmunk's eyes caught a slight movement. A slim, dark form was sneaking through the shadows and moving toward the burrow. A glance told the chipmunk of his danger. That long, slim body belonged to a weasel—his most dreaded enemy.

The weasel ran along with his nose close to the ground, following a trail made by the tracks of many creatures. Last evening the chipmunks had traveled this same path. Was it the scent of their tracks that the weasel was following?

Father Chipmunk fled back down the tunnel into the den. There he turned and looked up the long hallway, through which a faint light shone. It was only through this tunnel that the sly weasel could enter the den. As long as Father Chipmunk could still see that faint, round patch of light, he and his family would be secure from their enemy.

Father Chipmunk had been standing guard for only a moment when suddenly the patch of light was blacked out. The dread weasel was sneaking into the tunnel!

The old chipmunk did not hesitate for an instant. Barking a warning to arouse his family, he fled through the back tunnel to the secret door, where escape was possible.

Mother Chipmunk and the little ones awoke in terror and scurried after him. Their panic was so great that they scratched and clawed each other in their mad haste to escape through the secret door.

Each member of the family was now just a wild creature fighting to survive.

At the front door of the burrow the weasel was struggling, too. The tunnel that led from the doorway to the den was tight, even for his slim body. He had to squirm and twist to force his way in, but he managed to make his way along by going very slowly. He had forced his way into tight places before, and this one promised to provide him with a tasty meal.

His small, greedy eyes shone cruelly as his keen nose caught the scent of the chipmunks' tracks. The farther he squirmed into the narrow tunnel, the stronger the scent became—a sign that a number of chipmunks were living here.

But when he reached the den, it was empty! The chipmunks had fled. Only their tracks now remained, and these led the weasel to the narrow secret tunnel.

Eagerly snuffing at the tracks, he forced his way into this tunnel and started toward the back door. He had only to follow these tracks, and sooner or later they would lead him to his prey. Inch by inch he squirmed his way toward the secret door through which the chipmunks had fled.

Bushy Tail had been the last one out of the tunnel. When he found himself among the weeds outside the back door, he was filled with a new terror, for his family had vanished completely.

The weasel was coming, and the lone little chipmunk was in dreadful danger. In a flash Bushy Tail streaked down the hillside.

The bright moon shed its light over the forest and cast mysterious shadows on the chipmunk's path. This increased his panic, and he ran as he had never run before. Just ahead he saw an old hollow tree. Among its roots were many familiar hiding places.

Once nestled in one of these, he would be secure. If only he could get there in time!

Suddenly Bushy Tail paused to look back. What he saw aroused fresh terror in him. He was afraid to budge. Close behind him, in the dark shadow of an oak tree, two small greedy eyes gleamed through the darkness. The cruel, crafty weasel was near and would soon pounce upon him.

All at once the silence of the night was shattered by the fierce hunting cry of a great horned owl. The bird swooped from the giant oak like a swiftly passing shadow. Straight as an arrow it dived at those two shining eyes. There was a rustling in the shadows, and then all was still. The cruel weasel would prowl no more, for the owl had seized its prey.

No harm would come to Bushy Tail now as he raced toward a burrow in the roots of the old hollow tree. He reached the entrance and started inside. Then his nose caught a familiar scent that caused him to pause and twitch his tail in quick little jerks. Bushy Tail had found his family!

# The Partridge Family

## Mother Partridge Fools the Fox

Down the side of a wooded slope Mother Partridge led her baby chicks toward the meadow and the sparkling brook. Today, for the first time, she was taking her brood to drink.

Mother Partridge walked slowly, watching every bush and tree for dreaded enemies. Softly she clucked to the twelve wee babies that toddled after her on their tiny pink legs. They peeped anxiously whenever they were left even a few inches behind.

From "Redruff," in *Wild Animals I Have Known;* published by Charles Scribner's Sons. By permission of the publishers.

Mother Partridge was on the alert for her enemies, and just as she reached the bottom of the wooded slope, she saw one. Across the meadow a fox was sneaking toward her. If his keen nose caught the partridge•scent, he would surely pounce on her babies.

"Krrr! Krrr!" *Hide! Hide!* she warned the chicks, and they obeyed promptly, without panic. One hid under a leaf, another ran between two roots, and a third crawled into a hole. Soon all were hidden but one. He squatted on a chip of wood and sat motionless, looking almost like the chip itself.

Meanwhile the wise mother partridge flew directly toward the fox. A short distance from her enemy, she flung herself to the ground and flopped as if she were injured.

By pretending to be injured, she was going to lead Mr. Fox away from her brood. If she succeeded and then saved herself, the partridge family would survive this threat.

When the greedy fox saw a partridge near him, he sprang at the bird. But just as he almost had her, she arose and flew out of his reach. A moment later she sank to the ground, where she lay flopping and whining.

The fox leaped again and would have caught her, but Mother Partridge suddenly arose, pretended to falter, and then dragged herself away and hid near a hollow log.

The fox snapped his jaws and bounded over the log, while she made another forward jump and flung herself down a bank. For some mysterious reason, the farther the fox chased her, the faster she went, always increasing the distance between them.

The crafty fox was not accustomed to being fooled. In all this time the sly prowler had failed to catch a bird whose wing seemed to be injured! And most mysterious of all, instead of growing weaker, Mother Partridge apparently was gaining strength.

After leading the fox a safe distance away from the wooded slope where her family was hidden, the mother partridge suddenly arose. She swept off into a thicket, which concealed her.

The old fox had been completely fooled. He went slinking away, and danger no longer threatened the partridge family.

Whir-r-r! Mother Partridge flew back to the place where her tiny chicks lay hidden and stood quietly for a moment.

Even at her approach not one of her babies budged an inch. Not a single one of them uttered a peep. The little fellow squatting on the chip of wood just closed his eyes a bit tighter, until the mother said, "K-reet!" *Come, children!*

From hiding places all around toddled the baby partridges. The wee one on the chip opened his eyes and ran to his mother. One tiny chick crawled out of a hole, another scurried from under a leaf, and from among the roots of a tree came two more. Then all the other chicks came running, and the partridge family was united once more.

## The Chicks Learn Some Lessons

The midmorning sun was hot, and there was an open space to cross on the way to the brook. The mother spread her tail like a fan, and the chicks toddled along in its shadow. Walking slowly Mother Partridge was able to shield her brood from the rays of the scorching sun until they reached the thicket by the brook.

Then the mother bird dipped her beak in the pure, cool water, lifted her head, and swallowed. Presently one bold little chick ventured to dip his beak, then another, and soon every little partridge was dipping his beak, lifting his head, and drinking.

Then Mother Partridge led her brood to the green meadow. Here she was fortunate, for she found an ants' nest, that would provide food for her hungry babies. She stepped on the mound and raked it with her claws.

The big ant hill was broken open, and at once the ants swarmed out. Some ran around the mound, and others began carrying off the fat white cocoons containing the baby ants.

Mother Partridge seized one of these fat, tempting-looking cocoons and clucked. Then she dropped it, clucked, seized it again, and finally swallowed it. The tiny chicks stood watching, alert to her every movement.

Presently one little fellow—the one that had squatted on the chip—picked up a fat cocoon, dropped it, picked it up, and then he swallowed it. He had learned how to eat the cocoons. Soon all the others had learned.

The greedy chicks fought over the choice bits of food which their mother sent rolling down the big ant hill. By and by the young partridges had swallowed so many cocoons that they could eat no more.

Mother Partridge now led her brood up the stream. On a quiet, sandy bank, concealed by bushes, they lay all that afternoon. Only the occasional hum of a bee disturbed them. It was pleasant to feel the fine, cool sand running between their hot little toes as they squatted by their mother and scratched with their tiny feet.

That night Mother Partridge took her tired little ones to a sheltering thicket. There, among the dry leaves and twigs beneath the bushes, she folded them securely under her wings. The wee babies snuggled against her warm body, uttering soft little peeping sounds as they went to sleep.

## A Wild Colt's Lesson

War Paint was a wild colt whose spotted hide looked as if brushfuls of paint had been flung over his back and sides and over his dainty ears. The frisky colt roamed the vast western plains with a herd of wild horses, as free as the wind.

With the other wild colts, young War Paint romped nimbly up and down the steep sides of the canyons, kicking up his heels in fun. The favorite sport of the colts was a kind of boxing. They stood on their hind legs and pawed at each other awkwardly.

This romping sport helped the youngsters to become sure-footed and to defend themselves when danger threatened.

Frequently during their play the lively colts would pause, snatch a mouthful or two of grass, and then romp off again. This would continue until the colts tired of their sport, and then they would settle down to steady grazing close to the herd.

One day War Paint and his partner, Nosey, ventured off to explore a deep gully. They had not gone very far when War Paint heard his mother nicker to him. Nosey ambled on, looking back as if to say, "Oh, come along, and let's see what's in this gully." So War Paint did not heed the black mare's warning nicker. He galloped after Nosey.

The colts had gone only a short distance into the gully when a stone came rattling down a bank. The startled colts whirled. There stood a prairie wolf, ready to pounce!

Instantly the colts wheeled and started back toward the herd, but the wolf cut in ahead of them. Then the youngsters bolted to seek escape up the rocky cliff. Nosey deserted his partner and leaped nimbly up the gully to safety. War Paint started, but again the wolf headed him off.

Terrified, the spotted colt dodged, but the crafty gray beast dodged, too, and lunged in fury to cripple War Paint's hind leg. Quickly the colt lashed out with his nimble heels to defend himself.

291

War Paint saved his legs, but the powerful jaws of the wolf raked his side. Squealing with pain the colt fled, clattering over the rocks. War Paint's adventure had become a desperate fight for life.

Now the killer made a savage thrust at the colt. The wounded youngster was wild with terror, for he was cornered again. The wolf lunged once more, but fortunately War Paint leaped high into the air just as the wolf hurled himself forward.

The gray wolf was so intent on his victim that he had not heard the pounding of hoofs on the rim of the canyon. Suddenly a black thunderbolt shot down the side of the rocky cliff. With ears laid back, eyes flashing, and teeth bare, War Paint's mother plunged to his rescue.

The wolf was caught completely off guard. He had not the slightest chance to escape. With a lightning-like thrust, the enraged mare lunged forward and sank her teeth into the wolf's skin. Then with a quick toss of her head, she flung him end over end into a thicket of sharp-thorned cactus. He lay quite still, apparently injured.

Fully aroused, the black mare plunged after her victim, her eyes gleaming with savage fury. Her slashing forefeet were powerful weapons, ready to trample the dread enemy and teach him the lesson that he deserved. But just in time her victim got to his feet and managed to slink off among the rocks.

War Paint's mother did not try to follow him. Instead, she turned to her trembling colt and nickered. When he nickered in reply, she nosed over him gently.

As soon as the mare found that her colt was not badly injured, she snorted loudly as if to scold him. Then she gave him a little nip on his shoulder and nudged him gently on the forehead as if to say, "Now, my son, I hope you've learned your lesson."

# Gray Wing and Nika

## An Interrupted Flight

From their wilderness home in the north a wedge of splendid big Canada geese was winging its way southward.

Led by a wise old gander, they flew over mountains and shining rivers. Straight to a lake, hidden deep in a forest, the gander piloted his flock of sixty geese. Each year they rested on this lake for a day or two before continuing their flight to their winter feeding grounds. This lake had always been as secure as their northern wilderness home.

In this big wedge of soaring Canadas flew Gray Wing, a fearless young gander. His back and wings were darker than those of his companions. His pure white waistcoat and glossy black neck gleamed in the rays of the western sun. Flying near Gray Wing was graceful Nika, his mate.

When the geese were directly over the lake, the V-shaped wedge spread out, and the birds settled swiftly upon the calm water of this quiet place.

At dawn the geese awoke. Paddling close to shore, they began to feed on the wild rice, which was plentiful that autumn season. Gray Wing and Nika swam about with the other geese, concealed by the morning mist. The gray birds were fearless, for they had never been disturbed on this peaceful lake.

Slowly the sky lightened. The mist began to rise, and the shoreline appeared. There, hidden in the tall grass, two men with guns were waiting. As the mist lifted, they saw the splendid flock of geese.

The hunters lost no time. Instantly two shots burst out. A great cry arose from the startled geese, and with a heavy rustling of wings they beat their way upward through the rising mist in swift, desperate flight.

At a second burst of shot the big geese mounted rapidly. Above their outcry rose the clear call of the old gander, their leader. High overhead these splendid birds circled and headed southward through the shielding mist. Of the sixty geese, all were in the V-shaped wedge but three, and one of these was Nika.

At the first burst of shot, a splendid goose had flopped head downward into the water, a huddle of limp, gray feathers. Another bird had faltered and dropped when the guns blazed away the second time.

At that moment, Nika, rising swiftly from the lake, had felt a dull blow on her left wing, followed by a quick stab of pain. She faltered, then steadied herself, and attempted to beat her way upward.

But she could not reach her place in the swiftly-flying wedge. She called out to the flock, but only Gray Wing, her mate, heeded that wild cry. Looking back he discovered that Nika was absent from the wedge.

Uttering an answering cry, Gray Wing turned, left his place in the flying wedge, and came winding down toward Nika. By this time she was barely above the treetops, for the pain in her crippled wing was increasing.

From the misty sky the honking of the departing flock came back, high and clear. Then fainter and fainter came the cries as the big gray geese soared on. Gradually the sounds died away.

By this time Nika's strength was spent. So the two geese dropped to a small pond, where the reeds and rice concealed them.

Fortunately only Nika's wing was injured, but she was weak from the stabbing pain. When she had recovered some of her strength, the geese began to feed on the wild rice.

It was midmorning when a few tame ducks from a nearby farm came to the pond. They were marching in a single line, close behind a handsome green-headed drake. Gray Wing and Nika watched as the ducks and the big drake waded out into the water. Presently the northern birds ventured out from among the rice stalks and reeds near the shore and swam with the tame fowls.

Young Frank Gordon lived with his aunt
and uncle on a farm near the pond. Late
that afternoon Frank drove a herd of cows
to water near the place where Gray Wing and
Nika swam with the ducks.

Alarmed by the noise, Gray Wing rose up.
Nika's attempt to follow was in vain. Her
crippled wing could not bear her weight.

Gray Wing wheeled and flew back to Nika. Again they hid in the reeds near the shore.

Frank Gordon hurried to the farmhouse to tell his Aunt Lizzie and Uncle Peter about the big gray geese. When Aunt Lizzie heard his report, she promptly ordered that the visitors were not to be harmed.

Next day Frank took corn from the crib and scattered it near the pond where the gray strangers could find it. As he watched the splendid birds, he wished he could make pets of them.

The two geese ate the grain and remained among the wild rice and reeds while Nika's wing mended. Gradually it grew stronger, but Nika could not yet fly with her mate. After frequent attempts to lead her away, Nika's faithful partner always came back to her.

One morning the two gray Canadas were aroused by the distant honking of a flock of geese that were departing southward. Nika made an attempt to rise and join them, but she could not, and faithful Gray Wing did not desert her. He stayed with her, ready to assist her or to shield her from harm.

# Escape at Last

The last days of autumn passed swiftly. Then one night a storm swept in from the northwest, followed by a day of sleet and bitter cold. Aunt Lizzie Gordon thought at once of the big gray geese. They must be sheltered from the storm's fury. So Frank went out and coaxed the birds into a pen by carefully leaving a trail of corn.

Now the geese were robbed of their freedom. But they were safe with the other fowls, and as the season advanced, they seemed to get accustomed to their pen. Frequently they were allowed to run loose in the barnyard, and they came fearlessly at Frank's call.

Uncle Peter grumbled because the fowls ate so much grain, and once he suggested roast goose for Christmas. But Aunt Lizzie gave him such a scolding that he quickly insisted it was only a joke. And that was his last remark about roast goose.

One morning there was a wild honking in the barnyard. Nika was trying her wings! For more than fifty yards she circled upward. Then she dropped swiftly to the ground.

By the end of winter Nika had recovered from her wound and was able to fly again. So both geese were kept penned up.

On the first warm spring day Nika and her mate grew restless, longing for the freedom of their far northern home.

Suddenly a familiar call came from the sky, and a flying wedge of Canada geese swept directly overhead. They were returning from their winter far in the south.

Their silvery tones urged Gray Wing and Nika to join their flight to freedom. The two geese hissed in their prison yard and beat their splendid wings against the wire. But it was in vain. They could not escape.

Nearly a week afterward, a terrific gale struck suddenly during the night, causing damage on the farm. Large branches were torn from the trees, shingles were blown off the farmhouse roof, and the weather vane was twisted off the barn.

When Frank Gordon awoke next morning, he heard the fowls making a big commotion. Dressing quickly he hustled out to the shed where the gray Canadas were kept at night. There he saw that the gale had hurled a big limb of a tree against the door, completely shattering it. The prisoners had escaped.

Then far overhead, Frank's ears caught a faint honking, and immediately he heard loud answering cries from Nika and Gray Wing. He looked up just in time. Upward swept the two big birds to join the wedge of Canadas. Up, up they went—flying free at last.

## Smoozie the Reindeer

### Smoozie Takes a Journey

When Smoozie had gone to sleep, the Yukon River country had been green, just as the little fawn had always known it. But during the night the first snowfall of the season had come to that part of Alaska. And in the morning when Smoozie awoke, everything was covered with a pure white blanket of soft snowflakes.

Jumping up, Smoozie licked the feathery flakes from his dainty leg. He stretched himself and romped off to his mother, who had spied tender twigs peeping out of the snow. The fawn had a fine breakfast.

Soon Smoozie and his mother started up to the foothills, the fawn following in the doe's tracks. Ever since he could first walk, his mother had trained him to step in her footprints. So now Smoozie could easily make his way through the deep snow. Where the trail was rough, the doe would pick a secure foothold, then look back to make sure that Smoozie was safe before going on.

They climbed gradually upward, and by midmorning they came out on a rocky ledge where they lay down and drowsed awhile. When they awoke, they peered down the steep slope to the Yukon River. Far below them they saw moose that had stopped to drink.

Then something moved in the bare willows by the river. It was a reindeer herd on its yearly journey to the wooded hills to find shelter and food for the winter. Leading the herd was Ogg, a handsome stag.

Smoozie's mother watched restlessly for a brief moment. Then she nudged the fawn and led him down to join the herd. Onward they marched over the flat plain along the Yukon River into the blackness of the night.

There was no moon to light the way, but the stars shone brightly. By morning Smoozie was drooping with weariness, but still they pressed onward, advancing at a steady pace.

Late the next day the herd came to a bend in the river. Ogg, the big stag, plunged in, followed by the others, their antlers rising like a forest above the icy water. Smoozie jumped in bravely, but other fawns hesitated until their mothers nudged them. Then they finally plunged in and swam across, timid and shivering.

The journey to the winter feeding grounds was very hard on Smoozie and the other fawns. They were not accustomed to marching at a steady pace for hours without ceasing. Nor were they accustomed to leaping over gullies and scrambling over rocky ledges.

A few days before the herd reached the end of the trail, a blizzard struck the Yukon region. The bitter wind and swirling sleet dazed and blinded Smoozie, even though his mother tried to shield him with her body. If he had not known how to follow in her footsteps, the little fawn would not have been able to survive the journey.

As the fury of the blizzard increased, that northern region became a vast white wilderness. Yet in spite of the drifting snow, the reindeer jogged along at a steady pace. At last they came to a wide, rocky ledge that provided protection from the bitter wind.

Gradually the blizzard died away, and soon the drooping beasts found places to lie down and rest. Smoozie, as always, cuddled up to his mother. He lay there, snuggling close to the pleasant warmth of her body and slept.

## The Herd Fights for Its Life

The tired fawn's sleep was brief, however, for soon a long, dismal howl shattered the silence. Aroused and terrified, little Smoozie struggled to his feet and stood beside his mother for protection. His weary legs, not yet rested after the long journey, trembled so that he could scarcely stand.

The piercing howls came closer as wolves sneaked in from the hills. Then the snarls of the wolves mingled with the grunts of the reindeer. The wolf pack was closing in.

The dismal howls in the distance became ugly snarls near at hand as the lean, hungry wolves came slinking close for the attack.

Meanwhile the larger reindeer had begun circling about the youngsters. Smoozie and the other fawns were herded close together in the center of a moving mass of deer. Pressing closely about them were the older fawns and the mothers. Whirling on the outside of the mass were Ogg and the other stags. It was all accomplished without any difficulty and went on as smoothly as it if had been practiced for weeks.

The great mass now paced in one big circle. The faster it went, the more difficult it was for the wolves to sneak through that ring of flying legs and attack their prey.

Unless a wolf were desperately hungry, he would not risk being trampled by the sharp hoofs of those forefeet. Nor would he dare to get in the way of the slashing antlers.

The dizzy circling did not cease for even the briefest moment. Smoozie was confused by the whirling movement, and he was so tired that he almost dropped in his tracks.

A fearful bark pierced the air. Then came a moan as a valiant stag faltered and fell. The wolves had found a victim!

Suddenly Smoozie felt the circle pressing to one side. The whirling mass had moved away from the fallen reindeer so that the flying feet would not stumble over him.

Poor Smoozie dug his hoofs deep into the snow to keep from being upset. Suddenly a wounded deer hurled itself against him, and he was thrown over. He struggled to rise, but sharp hoofs cut into his sides, stomach, and forehead. He moaned in blinding pain.

Smoozie's ears caught a confused mingling of grunts, moans, and piercing howls as the terrific battle raged about him.

Then as suddenly as it had begun, the wild howling of the wolves ceased. Their snarls became distant echoes as the cruel beasts went slinking off. The battle was over.

Smoozie got tremblingly to his feet. Near him stood Ogg. The valiant stag had been wounded, but he held his antlers high as he looked over his herd that was now at peace.

# The Polar Bear Twins

## Lost on the Ice

In the arctic region of snow-covered ice near the North Pole, Fluffy and Tuffy, the polar bear twins, lived with their mother.

Their home was an immense ice pack. This mass of jagged ice covered a vast area in the Arctic Ocean, up near the top of the world.

It was October, and the sun shone only a very brief time each day in that wilderness region of snow and ice. So now the polar

From *The Polar Bear Twins*, by Jane Tompkins, published by Frederick Stokes Co.

bear twins did not feel the sun's warmth as they had in the springtime. But their thick fur coats kept them snug and warm as they romped and played in the snowdrifts.

Their mother guarded them carefully. She gave them milk and fed them seal meat when they were hungry. So the little twins had always been comfortable and secure in their arctic home.

One afternoon as the cubs slept calmly in the shelter of a snowbank, the mother bear opened her eyes, stretched, and then sniffed eagerly. No enemy scent disturbed her, and no whimpering came from her sleeping cubs. So the big, shaggy bear lumbered off across the ice to catch a seal.

A long time later Fluffy opened her eyes. Icy blasts of wind made her shiver. So she buried her little black nose in her fur and squirmed about to make herself comfortable. But she missed the warmth of her mother's massive body, and she whimpered drowsily.

Half asleep, she tried to snuggle up to her big, shaggy mother, who wasn't there. Tuffy moaned softly as he dozed. But their mother did not return to care for her children, and the little polar bears kept getting more and more restless. The sound of waves beating against the jagged ice confused and frightened them, for the water had been far away when the cubs had gone to sleep.

Both the little bears were now fully awake. Anxiously they sniffed the place where their mother had been lying before they went to sleep. Tuffy ran all around, looking for her. But he looked in vain.

The wind whistled, and snow drifted down on the twins. The booming of the massive ice cakes being broken up by arctic waves sounded like thunder in their ears. Fluffy, still whimpering, cuddled up to Tuffy.

Tuffy could do nothing to comfort little Fluffy, for he, too, was afraid. They dozed, woke up again, and finally fell fast asleep.

When Fluffy and Tuffy awoke, they were almost buried in a snowdrift. The storm was over, and the rays of the pale sun shone feebly. Shaking the snow away, the two cubs scrambled from their snug nest. Tuffy stood on his hind legs, trying to catch a glimpse of his mother, but the shaggy bear was nowhere to be seen.

All around them lashed the restless, blue water. The piece of ice on which they had been sleeping had broken away from the main ice pack, and Fluffy and Tuffy were floating out in the ocean on their own little island. They were lost on the vast arctic sea.

When the sun had set, they were still lost. They had no one to give them food. There was no great, shaggy body to snuggle against in the darkness for warmth and comfort.

Tuffy found a spot behind a mound of snow out of the wind's cold blasts, and here the twins cuddled down. They dozed now and then while they waited for their mother.

The north wind howled, and the jagged ice cakes boomed and hissed as they crashed into the little island. Fluffy and Tuffy moaned in their loneliness. They were hungry, but they tried hard to sleep while they drifted about on the foaming waves.

### Found At Last

Meanwhile the twins' mother had found a fat seal. After she had eaten a big meal of fresh seal meat, she began to feel very lazy.

She wanted to lie down and doze, but Fluffy and Tuffy must be fed. So she set out for the spot where she had left them sleeping.

The wind had now risen to a fierce gale, and snow had begun to drift. The big bear fought her way through mounds of snow and toiled untiringly over jagged peaks of ice.

Finally she came to the edge of the main ice pack. The twins were nowhere in sight. She stood up, sniffed the cold, frosty air, and looked out over that vast area, trying to locate her absent babies.

She wrinkled her black nose and sniffed. Fluffy and Tuffy were nowhere in sight, and she could not catch their scent. She called again and again, but there was no answer.

Finally the mother bear hurled herself into the foaming, icy water. With long, powerful strokes she swam first to one island of ice and then to another, looking for her cubs. For without her to guard them and give them food, the little polar bears could not survive.

All through the long night she hunted. All the next day she toiled over the ice and explored the cold blue waters.

All day and all night the anxious mother searched without rest. She refused to eat. Late on the second day she heard a sound like a faint whimper. Was it the cry of little Fluffy? Eagerly she swam toward the sound. But when she came to the place, she saw nothing. It was only the howling of the wind.

Finally the mother bear swam back to the main ice pack. She climbed to a high ledge nearby and looked over the lonely area. But her tired eyes caught no glimpse of her absent children.

It was midnight of the second day when the wind brought to her keen nostrils a faint scent of her cubs. She followed the scent to the water's edge, dived in, and began to swim rapidly.

Far out in the water she could just see an island of floating ice. As she drew nearer, the scent became much stronger. There could be no mistake—her toiling search was finally ended.

She swam directly to the ice and drew her massive body up out of the water. There lay little Fluffy and Tuffy, cuddled together beside a big mound of snow, sound asleep!

The mother buried her nose in their fur, waking Fluffy and Tuffy at the same instant. Then their mother nudged them and licked them with her long, rough tongue.

The little bears jumped up and licked their mother's face. They tugged at her shaggy body and nipped her ears gently. It was wonderful having their mother back again!

# Johnny's Alligator

Ever since Johnny's big brother Henry had caught and tamed an alligator, Johnny had wanted one, too. Today he intended to get it.

After breakfast he sat on the front steps of his farm home, close to the Santee River swamps, idly munching peanuts. Now and then Johnny tried roping the front gatepost. He pretended that it was the alligator he was going to catch.

Tiring of this sport, he coiled the rope, tossed it over his shoulder, and ambled out through the gate, singing.

Johnny sang loud, so that his mother would not discover he was absent from the porch. Then maybe she wouldn't guess he was taking the winding trail to the swamps. Johnny's mother had frequently warned him never to venture alone into the Santee swamps.

When he had walked far enough so that he was certain he could not be seen from the house, he commenced to go faster.

"I hope my 'gator won't be hiding in his cave under the riverbank," Johnny said to himself. "If he is, I'll just have to wait until he decides to come out."

As he hurried along, Johnny tried to recall all the exciting things Henry had told him about alligators. At the same time, however, he could not help feeling a little worried because he had not heeded his mother's stern warning about the swamps.

"If Henry can catch a 'gator, I guess I can, too. There's nothing to be afraid of in the swamp." Johnny spoke out loud. Listening to his own voice gave him courage, and so he whistled and hummed, too. Before long he reached the swamp.

Johnny strolled along beneath the lacy, moss-hung cypress trees. He smelled the fragrant blossoms of the tupelo trees, where bees were gathering honey. His keen glance darted about, alert to catch all the other wonderful sights of the swamp.

He saw a turtle sunning itself on a log and tossed a stick at it. Then he came to a clump of huckleberry bushes heavy with ripe, juicy huckleberries. On any other day nothing could have kept Johnny from a huckleberry bush. Today, however, he was

after his 'gator. So he paused just long enough to snatch a double fistful of those tasty huckleberries and then went on.

He saw bees buzzing about a hollow tupelo tree, and he wondered if that was where they had stored their honey. He'd come back later and find out, for no honey is sweeter than tupelo honey from the swamps.

"Ah, coon tracks!" he said, as he spied tiny footprints. "I'll come back here this winter. If he's a big coon, and if I sneak up on him and catch him, I'll trade him to Henry for his fiddle. Henry wants a coon hide." Then he forgot about the coon, for he had seen his 'gator.

It was a river alligator, about four feet long—just the size he could handle. It was slithering through the broom grass toward the river. Johnny was lucky. He had not expected to find his 'gator out of water.

When the alligator saw Johnny, it stopped dead still and lay like an old cypress log.

Johnny advanced very cautiously, getting his rope ready to throw. But the alligator saw Johnny coming and slithered off toward the riverbank again.

Johnny coiled his rope and threw it, but it caught on a tupelo tree. While he was getting the rope untangled, the alligator had advanced several yards toward the river.

Again Johnny tried, and again he missed. He was ready to try a third time, when he heard a warning rattle from behind a cypress log. Glancing around he saw five feet of coiled rattlesnake and a wide, wicked head. The snake hissed, and Johnny got away fast.

He didn't stop to kill the snake, for he knew that his 'gator was heading straight for the deep swamp water, with only a few yards to go. Once again Johnny threw his rope. This time it landed squarely about the alligator's thick neck. Johnny felt mighty proud. Now he could tow his prize home. He would show Henry!

The alligator fought against the rope and flopped about, trying to get loose. Johnny gripped the towing rope tighter and tugged hard as the alligator struggled to free himself from the rope.

Suddenly the alligator hooked his big tail around a cypress tree, and Johnny couldn't budge him. He just lay there and stared at Johnny with his unblinking, snakelike eyes.

Henry had said that if a 'gator makes up his mind he won't budge, he just won't. And so Johnny calmly sat down to wait till his 'gator would unhook.

Johnny still gripped the rope, but he was keeping out of reach of that slashing tail. An alligator defends itself by slapping with its tail. And its slap is no gentle pat.

Finally the alligator unhooked his tail, and
once more Johnny tried to tow the beast.
He was watching the alligator so intently
that he did not notice something moving in
the bushes nearby.

Then the bushes parted, and the ugly head
of a wild pig peered out. Her eyes gleamed
wickedly, and she uttered furious grunts.

Panic seized Johnny as the pig opened her
ugly, foaming mouth. He looked desperately
for a tree, but none was near enough to
climb before that wild pig could reach him.
His grip on the towing rope tightened.

Now Johnny wished that he had heeded his mother's warning never to go into the swamp alone. He knew now why his mother had said the Santee swamps were dangerous. After this, Johnny certainly would listen to his mother's warnings.

Suddenly the angry pig lunged at him, her savage jaws dripping with foam. By good luck, Johnny had walked just far enough so that his alligator was between him and the pig. Apparently the pig was so intent on the boy that she hadn't seen the alligator. Just as she got within reach, the beast gave a swift, easy flip of his tail, and the wild pig tumbled over.

As the pig got up and tore madly into the swamp, Johnny laughed out loud. He felt much better. He was thankful to be alive.

Slowly he began coiling his long rope and walking directly toward the alligator's head. He knew that the 'gator's tail could not reach him if he kept in front of the beast. Finally Johnny got up to him and began rubbing his hand around and around on the tough, leathery head. For Henry had said, "A 'gator likes to be petted."

The alligator's jaws fell open, and his eyes closed sleepily.

"I've changed my mind about you," declared Johnny as he slipped the rope off the thick neck. "You're my 'gator, all right, but you saved my life, and you deserve to stay right here. You'd miss this old Santee swamp."

Then Johnny started for home, singing, and his 'gator slithered off through the grass.

# Famous People
## of Other Times

# Joseph and His Brothers

## The Coat of Many Colors

Long, long ago, in Bible times, there lived a lad named Joseph who had eleven brothers. Their father, Jacob, owned large flocks of sheep and goats, and it was the duty of the ten elder brothers to guard the flocks as they roamed from pasture to pasture.

The baby Benjamin was too young to tend the flocks, and Jacob frequently kept Joseph at home also. These two sons were free to run and play about their father's tent, while the others worked hard.

The elder brothers were jealous of Joseph and said that their father loved him best. And indeed this was true, for Jacob showed that he favored the boy by giving him a handsome coat of many colors. Joseph loved its gay stripes of red, blue, and yellow, and he wore it every day.

None of the elder brothers had such a fine coat. When they saw it, they envied and hated Joseph still more.

One morning Joseph told his brothers of a strange dream. "I dreamed," he said, "that it was the season of harvest, and we were all together in the fields, binding grain. I bound up my sheaf of grain and laid it down, as you did yours. Then my sheaf arose and stood upright, and all your sheaves arose and bowed low before it."

"Ho!" laughed one brother scornfully. "I suppose you think that one day *we* shall have to bow down to *you!*"

The others echoed his scornful laugh, and they hated Joseph more than ever, for they feared that the boy's dream might indeed be fulfilled.

The next night Joseph dreamed that the sun, the moon, and eleven stars bowed before him. When he awoke and told his dream, his elder brothers were so ill-tempered and jealous that they refused to speak to him.

Jacob spoke sternly to Joseph for telling such foolish dreams. But in his own mind Jacob wondered if the dreams might truly have some meaning.

Soon after this the elder brothers departed with their flocks, in search of fresh pastures. Many days passed without word of them. One morning Jacob called Joseph to his tent and bade him set out to find his brothers.

"Bring me word whether all is well with my sons and with the flocks also," Jacob ordered, and he sent the lad off with his blessing.

So Joseph set out, wearing his coat of many colors. He walked a long way, for his brothers had gone far from home. At length he saw the flocks far off and hastened toward them, and when Joseph was yet at a distance, the brothers recognized him by his coat.

"Here comes that dreamer of dreams," said one jealously. And they all began planning how they might harm Joseph.

"Let us slay him and be rid of him," said a second brother. "Then we shall see if his dreams are fulfilled." Quickly they planned to slay Joseph and cast his body into a deep pit nearby.

"We can say a wild beast has devoured him," suggested a third, with an evil smile.

But Reuben, the eldest brother, begged the others to have mercy on the young dreamer and not slay him. At last they decided to throw Joseph into the pit without harming him. Reuben consented to this plan, and the others waited for Joseph's arrival.

Meanwhile Reuben wandered off and hid, for he intended to rescue the boy from the pit after the others had moved on.

Soon Joseph came up to his brothers, not fearing or expecting any danger. At once they stripped off his fine coat and lowered him into the pit before he could lift a hand to defend himself.

While the brothers were still laughing over their evil trick, they saw a caravan of camels and merchants drawing near them. The camels were loaded with bales of rich goods, for the merchants were on their way to the land of Egypt to trade in the markets. Instantly the jealous brothers had another

evil thought. Why not sell Joseph to these merchants as a slave? Then they would not be guilty of killing their brother, and they would receive payment for him besides.

The plan was no sooner thought of than it was accomplished, and they sold Joseph for twenty pieces of silver. After binding his hands with tough thongs, the merchants tied Joseph to a camel. Then the caravan went on its way westward toward Egypt.

At dusk Reuben made his way to the pit and called softly to Joseph. Great was his sorrow on finding the pit empty. And when he questioned his brothers, they pretended to know nothing about the lad.

Next day the brothers killed a young goat and dipped Joseph's coat in the blood, so that it would look as if he had been attacked by some wild beast.

When they reached home, they showed the blood-covered coat to Jacob, and he felt sure that his beloved son had been killed by a wild beast. Then Jacob went off by himself and wept for the son he had loved, and he refused to be comforted.

# The Famous Young Ruler

After many days' journey, the caravan of merchants, camels, and slaves came into the land of Egypt. There Joseph was sold as a slave to the Captain of the Guard at the King's palace.

Now the Captain of the Guard was a good judge of men, and he felt sure that Joseph was honest and could be trusted. Instead of sending Joseph out into the fields to labor with the other slaves, the Captain took Joseph into his home and made him his steward in charge of the household.

Year after year Joseph was trusted with more duties in his master's household, and he performed every duty faithfully and well. At last he was made chief steward in charge of the entire household, with all its slaves and servants, and of the farm lands as well. He learned the language of Egypt, and his master looked upon him with favor.

The Captain's wife grew jealous of Joseph's power and wanted to cause him trouble. She told her husband that his steward did evil things behind his back. And so the Captain punished Joseph by casting him into prison, where he was set at hard labor.

But even in prison Joseph showed that he was faithful and honest. The steward of the prison soon trusted him and granted him many kind favors. Before long Joseph was freed from hard labor and put in charge of the other prisoners, and whatever he did was done well.

There came a day when two of the King's attendants were cast into the prison. One night they each had a strange dream, which they told to Joseph. Then Joseph told them what the dreams meant, for God had given him the power and the wisdom to do this.

To one attendant he said, "In three days you shall be a free man."

And to the other attendant Joseph said, "In three days you shall be dead."

And both these things came to pass, just as Joseph had foretold.

Two long years went by, and then the King of Egypt dreamed two dreams in one night— dreams so strange that the King feared they foretold some dreadful happening.

In his first dream the King saw seven fat cows come out of the river and commence to graze on the bank. Then seven lean cows came up and devoured the fat ones.

In a second dream he saw seven full heads of grain clustered on one stalk. Instantly they were devoured by seven other heads of grain which were thin and withered. The King sent for the judges and other wise men and asked them to reveal the meaning of his dreams. But not one could reveal it.

Then the attendant who had been in prison told the King about Joseph. At once the King sent for him and told him the dreams.

And Joseph spoke to the King, saying, "The seven fat cattle and the full heads of grain stand for seven years in which the harvests shall be rich and of great plenty. But the seven lean cattle and seven withered heads of grain stand for the seven years following the rich years. These years shall be years of famine, in which no grain shall grow.

"Therefore let the King be warned. Let him gather up and store away one-fifth of all the grain that is harvested in the years of plenty. Then there will be food when the seven years of famine come. Also let the King appoint an officer who is both wise and honest to see that all this is accomplished."

The King and all his officers listened to Joseph and marveled at his wisdom.

Then the King said, "There is no other so wise as Joseph. Therefore I appoint him to be the officer. From this day forward he shall be in charge of the land of Egypt."

And so it was. The King gave Joseph his own ring, clothes of fine linen, and a gold chain to wear about his neck. Wherever he went, the people of Egypt bowed down to him and obeyed his word.

It came to pass that the next seven years were years of plenty, with rich harvests. And Joseph saw to it that one-fifth of the grain that was harvested was stored away.

## More Dreams Fulfilled

The years of famine came, just as Joseph had foretold. Not only in Egypt did famine come, but in several other countries beyond its borders. Then word spread far and wide that in Egypt there was grain to spare.

Thus it happened that caravans journeyed from other lands to buy grain in Egypt. With them came Joseph's ten elder brothers. The ten bowed before Joseph, pleading for grain, but they did not recognize him.

Joseph recognized them at once, and he recalled his dream, in which his brothers' sheaves had bowed down before his own.

Suddenly Joseph's heart sank with fear, for he realized that Benjamin was not there. Quickly he planned to test his brothers and discover if they had harmed Benjamin. He spoke roughly, accusing them of being spies.

"You came to see if we are so weakened by famine that you may attack us," he said.

Then Reuben spoke out, denying that they were spies. "We are the twelve sons of Jacob," he declared, "and men of truth."

"Do you say twelve?" Joseph questioned. "I count but ten."

Reuben replied, "One son is dead, and the twelfth is still at home with our father."

Joseph commanded, "Bring this twelfth brother to me. Thus will I know that you are men of truth and not spies."

Then Joseph bade the soldiers bind one brother and keep him in prison as a pledge that the others would return. The brothers talked among themselves, saying, "This is to punish us for the evil we did to Joseph."

Joseph gave no sign that he heard them. He accepted payment for the grain, but he ordered that the money be returned secretly. His servants filled sacks with grain, put the money inside, and sent the brothers off.

After a time the brothers returned, bringing Benjamin. Joseph wanted to embrace the youth, but he held back, wishing to test the others once again.

Therefore Joseph freed the brother who was in prison and invited all of them to his own house for a feast. He inquired earnestly concerning their father, and they marveled that a famous ruler should do this.

Once more Joseph ordered that his brothers' sacks be filled. But this time he concealed his own silver cup in Benjamin's sack. No sooner had the brothers departed, than he bade soldiers follow them and seize the thief who had stolen his cup.

The soldiers soon found the silver cup in Benjamin's sack. They said he had stolen it and ordered him to return. And the others, thinking of their aged father's love for the youth, returned also to beg for mercy.

One brother knelt before Joseph, pleading earnestly, "Spare this lad, I beg you. Make me your slave instead. For he is our father's beloved youngest son. One other son has he loved and lost, and to lose this one, also, would surely kill him."

Joseph wept with joy, for now he knew that his brothers were no longer jealous. In a trembling voice he revealed who he was.

Then Joseph sent for his father to come and live in the land of Egypt. So Jacob and all his sons and their families lived in peace and comfort throughout the years of famine and for many years thereafter.

# David the Shepherd Boy

## David and His Harp

In the Bible land where Joseph had lived as a boy, nearly everyone raised sheep. So nearly every young lad found his first work in caring for his father's flocks.

Long, long after Joseph's time a boy named David began tending his father's sheep when he was scarcely more than a child. Many a man spent his entire life tending sheep and lived until the end of his days in the humble tent where he had been born. But David's days did not end in a shepherd's tent, even though he loved his flocks.

David liked to sing to the music of his harp while the sheep grazed peacefully nearby. As his fingers touched the trembling strings, the music rang out pure and sweet.

Everyone who had heard David sing and play remembered his clear voice and the ringing notes of his harp.

Now the King of the land was weary from the many battles he had fought against his country's enemies, and his soul was troubled. Night after night King Saul could not sleep but lay tossing and moaning from dusk to dawn. Therefore he grew pale and ill.

"If only the King could sleep!" said his attendants over and over. Then one of them suggested that if soft music were played, King Saul might sleep peacefully. Then another one told of David and his harp. So the King sent for David and bade him come and play for him.

David's father gave him his blessing, and the lad departed on his errand of mercy. His harp was slung over one shoulder, and gifts for the King were in his donkey's saddlebags.

It was dark when David came to the palace of King Saul. Servants led him quickly to the King's room, where one lamp flickered feebly beside the low bed. The King tossed restlessly, moaning aloud in his distress.

Without a word, David began to play on his harp. The tune was soft and gentle—a tune that David had often played to quiet his frightened, bleating sheep.

At first King Saul seemed not to hear the music. But at length his restless, tossing figure lay still. By the dim light of the flickering lamp, David could see that the King's eyelids were drooping. David played on, singing softly the words that had come into his mind as he watched his sheep on the lonely hillside. The King's eyelids drooped lower. At last he slept.

Each night David played for King Saul, and each night the King slept peacefully.

In time a warm friendship grew between the King and the young shepherd boy. After awhile the King recovered, and he no longer needed David's music. So David was allowed to depart, and once more he set out, with his harp slung over his shoulder.

Soon his friendship with the King was almost forgotten, and again he was a humble shepherd boy, protecting his flocks. Many a lamb might have been stolen by the prowling beasts, but David always had his shepherd's staff and his sling ready for them.

David's arm was strong, and his aim was sure. When he sent a stone whirling from the leather thongs of his sling, it struck with terrific force. That summer he killed a lion and a bear with only the sling and his staff for weapons.

# David and Goliath

Meanwhile, David's elder brothers had left home to serve in King Saul's army. War had broken out with a neighboring country, and the armies were now camped near David's home.

One day David's father bade him take ten loaves of bread and a large measure of grain to the brothers. He also bade him take ten cheeses as a gift for their captain.

Now the army of King Saul was camped upon a mountainside, and the army of the enemy was camped upon another mountain opposite it, with a valley between. Neither army dared come down into the open valley, and so no great battle had yet been fought.

But each day a huge giant named Goliath came forth from the enemy camp, daring any man to come and fight him.

Boasting and bragging he roared out his challenge, "Appoint any man among you and let him come and fight me. If he be able to kill me, then all my people shall be your slaves. But if I kill him, your people shall be our slaves forever."

Daily he came forth, wearing heavy brass armor and a brass helmet and gripping a huge spear. Daily he roared out his challenge, but so great was his size that no one dared face him.

Now as David entered the camp, Goliath came striding forth from his tent, bragging and challenging as before. All the King's men drew back, afraid, and David inquired scornfully, "Does no one dare to accept the challenge?"

The soldiers were furious to hear a mere youth question their courage. Even David's brothers turned against him, saying, "Such words are not for a humble shepherd boy. Let a soldier judge a soldier."

King Saul heard of David's words, and he sent for the youth to bid him return home. But David stood bravely before the King, saying, "I will fight this giant, Goliath, since no one else will go against him."

Such courage pleased King Saul, although he was sure that it would take more than courage to kill Goliath. "A lad like you cannot fight a giant," he said kindly.

But David said, "As I watched my sheep, I killed a lion and a bear. Is this giant more to be feared than they? If God gave me strength to slay a lion and a bear, will He not also deliver me from your enemy?"

And Saul answered, "Go, then, and may God go with you."

Then King Saul gave his own helmet and his armor and sword to the fearless youth. But the weight of the armor was so great that David could scarcely move hand or foot.

"I cannot wear this," he said. "Let me go as I am and fight with my own weapons."

So the slim young lad went calmly forth to meet Goliath, his long staff in one hand and his sling in the other. From a brook he chose five smooth stones and slipped them into the pouch at his belt.

When Goliath saw David approaching with his shepherd's staff, he roared in a mighty voice, "Am I a dog that a boy comes with a stick to fight me?"

The giant lunged forward, ready to slay the lad with one blow of his huge spear.

But David had been putting a stone in his sling as he walked. Then taking a few quick running steps, he whirled the leather thongs so fast that they were a mere flash in the sunlight.

With a flick of his hand David loosed the stone and slung it straight to its mark upon Goliath's forehead. The huge giant fell to the earth, his brass armor and helmet crashing against the rocks.

When the enemy saw their champion fall, they fled in terror. King Saul's army rushed after them and drove them from the land, and there was great rejoicing over the victory.

So David became famous throughout the kingdom. And when Saul's days on earth were ended, David became the ruler. David was a great king and ruled his kingdom with wisdom and honor for many years. Thus it came to pass that David, the humble shepherd boy, ended his days in a king's palace and not in a shepherd's tent.

# Saint George

In olden days a young lad named George dreamed of the time when he would become a soldier. He longed to wear shining armor and to do brave deeds like the royal guards who fought for the King.

But George learned to fight long before he was old enough to be a soldier. He practiced hurling his spear until he could thrust it straight into the target while riding astride a galloping horse. When the King heard of the youth's skill, he appointed George one of his royal guards. George fought bravely for his King, winning victories and honor.

Now it happened that not far away lived a wicked Prince, who did not permit his subjects to worship God. If the Prince found any of his subjects worshipping God, he punished them cruelly. Some he even killed.

When George heard of this, he was filled with anger, for he honored and loved God, and he had vowed to champion His cause. "I will fight this evil Prince," he declared, "and I pray that God will assist me and give me the strength to overcome him."

So the young champion selected an army, and each of his men pledged allegiance to George and vowed to serve God and the right. George rode at their head, clothed in shining steel armor. On his left arm was a shield with a flaming scarlet cross, and his sword hung at his belt.

One evening, just at sunset, George halted his army at the top of a high cliff. There in the valley below them lay the city of the wicked Prince.

"Rest well and prepare yourselves for the battle," said George to his men. "Tomorrow we shall fight."

In the gray light of early dawn George and his gallant soldiers set forth. But news of their coming had gone ahead of them. As they reached the level plain outside the city, they saw an immense army ready for battle.

George did not falter, for he felt that God was with him. He rode steadily onward, and his gallant soldiers followed.

When he was within a spear's throw of the foe, George halted his steed. Boldly the wicked Prince roared out his challenge, "Who are you, and why do you come?"

George's voice rang out both loud and clear, "I am one who fights for the right! And I come against you in anger!"

As the ringing answer died away, George raised his spear aloft and charged forward.

The Prince's soldiers were so overcome by George's words and by the sight of his sturdy soldiers that they let their weapons fall from their hands. Fleeing back into the city, they abandoned their hated Prince, and he faced his foe alone.

When George's men beheld the fleeing foe abandoning their Prince, they withdrew, for a soldier of honor always fights fairly, only one against one. Then the Prince leaped to meet George's charge, and the two warriors came together so violently that their spears shattered into bits.

As the Prince seized a spear dropped by one of his men, a soldier quickly provided a spear for George. They charged and fought again, and again the spears met and shattered. They charged and fought seven times, and at the seventh charge they crashed like thunderbolts, and each one fell from his horse.

The Prince leaped to his feet and hurled himself violently forward while George was still on one knee.

Raising his sword aloft, the Prince dealt George such a fierce blow that the keen blade pierced his steel armor, and blood poured forth. But George dealt a harder blow in return, using his weapon with such skill that the Prince's blade flew from his hand.

"Yield to me," cried George. "Yield to me the victory in the name of the true God and make a vow as I tell you."

"What then shall I vow?" asked the Prince, overcome with shame.

Then George put up his own sword, saying, "Pledge allegiance to God and pledge to fight only for the right. Help women always and have pity on the poor and weak. Worship God faithfully and treat your subjects as you yourself would wish to be treated."

The Prince dropped to his knees and vowed to worship God and do as George had bidden him. Then the Prince offered George great wealth, but the noble champion refused it and asked that it be given to the poor.

The Prince took George and his army to his castle and entertained them until next morning, when they continued on their way.

Thus did George do his famous deeds, and he fought in many lands as champion of the poor, the crippled, and the helpless.

It is said that one day as he rode to a distant city, he beheld a beautiful young maiden weeping bitterly. George halted his steed and spoke to her with gentle pity.

Then the maiden told her sorrowful tale. A horrible beast called a dragon was raging over the countryside. It devoured sheep and cattle as a cat eats mice. Now the sheep and cattle were gone, and the beast was devouring the people one by one. No one was brave enough or strong enough to slay it.

"Weep no longer," said George, "for I will fight this dragon to the death."

Even as George finished speaking, a loud roar came from a nearby cave. The ground began to tremble violently as if there were an earthquake. Then an enormous dragon charged forth from its den.

With a mighty shout George galloped to meet the monster. He was upon it before the dragon could strike a single blow with its tremendous tail or horrible claws.

George dealt the dragon a powerful blow, thrusting his sword deep into the wicked beast. With one last bellow of rage the dragon fell dead, stabbed to the heart.

The people of the city rushed forth with loud rejoicing. They offered their champion great wealth, but he refused it, bidding them thank God for the victory. Then once more he set out in search of good deeds to do.

All his life he was so good and brave and true that he was named Saint George. And to this very day the name of Saint George stands for bravery, and tales of the famous soldier-saint are told in every land.

# Joan of Arc

### Joan Hears the Voices

More than five hundred years ago, in the little French village of Domremy, lived a young peasant girl named Joan of Arc. One sunny afternoon Joan sat tending a herd of goats and cattle. But she was not thinking of her work alone. Joan's mind was troubled, for her beloved country was at war.

"Thoughts of war are not for a girl," was her father's stern answer whenever Joan would ask questions concerning the battles. But Joan could not help thinking of how the war must sadden the young French king.

King Charles was not yet a real king. He could not rule the people of his beloved

France until he could go to the city of Reims and be crowned, as all French kings had been crowned for hundreds of years. Charles could not do this, because Reims and all the rest of northern France were held by the enemy.

Poor Charles was almost a prisoner in his own kingdom. His soldiers had lost so many battles that they had lost all courage, too. Even his most loyal subjects believed that the enemy would soon conquer all France.

Day after day as Joan watched the herd or went about her simple household tasks, she thought of her King. Often she prayed that God might help him. One noon as she knelt in the garden to pray, a great light shone all about her. Out of the light came voices so strangely sweet that Joan wondered whether she was awake or dreaming.

"Joan, Maid of France," the voices seemed to say, "be faithful and true, and you shall serve your King and save France."

Joan was frightened, but she was thrilled, too, for she felt sure that these mysterious voices came from heaven.

Time after time these heavenly voices told Joan that God had chosen her to save France. But how could a simple peasant maid save her country? Joan could think of only one way. She must go as a soldier and lead the French army to victory.

Joan did not dare tell her father of this plan. Many times he had said that a girl's place was at home, helping her mother. So she begged an older cousin to assist her.

The cousin listened in wonder as Joan related her story. He agreed to take her to a town near Domremy, where there was a nobleman called Sir Robert, a loyal friend of King Charles. Joan was very sure that this nobleman would make it possible for her to reach the King and tell him what the heavenly voices had revealed. But Sir Robert only laughed at Joan. She looked so young and childlike as she stood there in her simple peasant dress that he thought the tale of voices from heaven was only a dream.

"Take the silly girl home," he ordered in a harsh voice. Joan returned to Domremy, but she did not abandon her purpose.

After a time she went to Sir Robert again. "Send me to the King," she told him. "It is God's will." There was something in the tone of her voice that made him listen. At last he was convinced that she spoke the truth, and he consented to help her.

The people of the town were more easily convinced that God had intended this pure, sweet maid to save France. They gave their hard-earned money to buy boy's clothing for her, since she could not go to war dressed as a girl. Her cousin bought her a horse, and Sir Robert gave her a sword.

Then with two young noblemen and their servants for protection, Joan set forth, riding on her steed like any soldier. The way led through towns and cities that were held by the enemy. So Joan and her faithful guides followed side roads and narrow footpaths.

Frequently they traveled at night under the protection of darkness. In the daytime they hid in barns or haystacks.

## The Warrior Maid Fights for France

At last Joan reached the King. Eagerly she poured out her message from the voices, but King Charles did not trust this unknown girl. Someone whispered that Joan was a witch, and many were quite ready to believe this.

But finally Joan's earnest words and gentle manner convinced the King that she was indeed sent by God's command, and he put his army under her leadership.

Dressed in shining white armor, Joan rode forth to meet the foe. On her silken banner were lilies, the royal sign of France. Four thousand soldiers followed her.

Her purpose was to lead the King to Reims to be crowned, but first she must drive the enemy from all the towns and cities that lay between him and Reims. Boldly Joan led her army to the city of Orleans, commanding the enemy to abandon it.

Her foes were determined not to abandon Orleans without a battle. They withdrew to a large fort just beyond the walls and waited for Joan's army to attack.

The French people in Orleans were faithful subjects of King Charles, and they rejoiced at the Maid's coming. They flocked to fight beneath her lily banner, ready to save their beloved France or die.

Somehow, in the excitement, a company of French soldiers rushed out to attack the enemy without waiting for Joan's leadership. Their attack had begun while Joan was sleeping, but suddenly the Maid awoke as if she had been warned. Quickly she put on her armor and galloped to the battle front.

In a moment she was in the thickest of the fight. Holding her gleaming sword aloft she called out to the men, "Forward! Forward for France and victory!" Never did men fight more bravely. The courage of the Warrior Maid seemed to fill their hearts with hope and to lend their arms new strength. With eager lips the soldiers echoed Joan's valiant cry, "France and victory!"

When the foe beheld the slender figure in shining white, they quaked with fear. Some thought she was a saint, and others believed her a witch, but one and all they feared her power. Although they were frightened, the foe fought back savagely, and when darkness came, the French had not yet conquered them.

Two days later Joan led the French army in an attack on the fort itself. This was a daring plan, for even a handful of soldiers behind the fort's high walls could beat off a whole army on the ground below.

Straight to the very walls Joan led her soldiers, urging them forward with shouts of cheer and courage. Suddenly an arrow struck her with such force that it pierced her armor and sank deep into her shoulder. Weak with stabbing pain, Joan was carried from the field of battle.

Now it was the turn of the enemy to be filled with hope. The Maid might be a witch or even a saint, but at least she could be wounded like an ordinary person. Boldly they renewed the battle and dealt such sturdy blows that the French withdrew.

When Joan saw the French army falling back, she leaped to her feet. Giving no heed to the pain of her wound Joan seized her lily banner and waved it aloft.

"Forward!" she called in a voice ringing with courage. "For France and victory!"

At sight of her bravely flying banner, the French were filled with new courage. Once more under Joan's gallant leadership the French army charged and this time fought to victory. The battle of Orleans was won!

There were other cities to be conquered. Hard weeks of bloody fighting lay ahead, but with skill and daring the Maid pressed onward until the road to Reims was free.

Joan went to Charles, but the timid King did not trust the Maid to take him safely through a region where the enemy had been so powerful. However, Charles yielded to her wish and accompanied her to Reims. There he was crowned the King of France, while Joan of Arc stood beside him in triumph.

Joan longed to return to Domremy and become a humble peasant maid once more. But the army needed her leadership, and so again she set out to fight. This time victory was not to be hers, for she was captured and thrown into prison. She thought the King would rescue her, but he did not.

The enemy accused Joan of being a witch and treated her cruelly. "Confess you are a witch," they thundered at her. "Deny you heard voices from heaven." Joan would not deny it, but the judges decided she was a witch and ordered her burned to death.

Even at the moment of her death Joan uttered a prayer. Then the watching foe knew she was not a witch. "God have mercy on us," cried one. "We have burned a saint."

Thus died Joan of Arc, the Warrior Maid, and all France wept with shame and sorrow. But even in death Joan served her country. For the French soldiers, remembering the valiant Maid, rose to fight with new courage. Before many years had passed, they had won freedom for the land that Joan had loved better than her life.

# Old Tales
# from Everywhere

# Chanticleer and the Fox

Once upon a time a poor woman lived in a small cottage at the edge of a wood. She had little enough to eat, but she considered herself extremely well off to have a cow, a pig, and a few chickens.

Among her chickens was a very handsome rooster named Chanticleer. His comb was as red as fire, and his feathers were as yellow as gold. For loud and long crowing he had no equal in all the country round. And if there could ever be such a creature as the King of Roosters, Chanticleer certainly was that King.

One night as Chanticleer was perched by his wife in the chicken house, he began to moan and mumble in his sleep. Then he began to groan as if in great distress. He made such a fuss that his wife woke from her slumber and looked at him in great concern. "Chanticleer! Oh, Chanticleer!" she cried. "What is wrong with you?"

Her cries awakened Chanticleer, and he started up with a great fluttering of his wings. "Oh, my dear," he exclaimed, his red comb stiff with terror, "I've had the most horrible dream. You simply can't imagine how it frightened me."

In a quivering voice Chanticleer continued, "I was in the yard, scratching for food, when, lo! I beheld a strange beast lurking there.

"He looked like a dog, but his manner was extremely fierce. He was yellowish-red in color, and he had a long, plumy tail and a pointed snout. His eyes glowed like coals of fire, and his dismal howls were terrible to hear."

"Simpleton!" said Mrs. Chanticleer in a scornful voice. "Why make a fuss about a ridiculous dream! Everyone knows that dreams are caused by overeating and rich food. Really you are worse than a goose."

Such talk hurt Chanticleer's pride, and he began to relate all the dreams he had ever heard of that had been fulfilled. He tried to prove to his wife that dreams had often foretold very important matters, but she would not listen to him.

"Not *your* dreams," she said. "So quit fussing and sputtering and go back to sleep."

"Yes, my dear," said Chanticleer meekly, for he was too tired to keep on arguing. So they slumbered peacefully until morning.

At the first streak of light, Chanticleer was fully awake. He flew down from his perch and strutted out to the barnyard in a royal manner. With a flapping and fluttering of wings he hopped up to his accustomed perch on the fence and crowed:

"Cock-a-doodle-doo, cock-a-doodle-doo!
Time for work and breakfast, too."

All the hens came down from their perches, cackling loudly, and began to look for juicy insects to satisfy their appetites. The vain cock puffed up with pride as he saw how they scurried to obey him. He strutted up and down in the barnyard, his red comb standing up like a king's crown. Every time he ate an insect, he crowed loudly to remind the hens that his alert eye was upon them.

As the rays of the sun became hotter and hotter, Chanticleer decided he would stop looking for insects and take a dust bath. Hastily swallowing a cricket, he went down to the end of the garden fence, where the dirt was as loose as ashes. It was cool and dry and especially good for wallowing.

While Chanticleer was wallowing in the dust, a creature with yellowish-red fur, a long, pointed snout, and a plumy tail came slinking through the gate.

Now Chanticleer did not know it, but this was a sly old fox. He had been lurking in the bushes all morning, waiting for just this opportunity to catch Chanticleer away from the hens.

"I bid you good morning, Mr. Chanticleer," said the wily fox, regarding the cock with watchful eyes.

Chanticleer started up in terror as he beheld the horrible creature of his dreams, but the wily fox was speaking again before Chanticleer had recovered from his fright.

"Now, sir, don't be afraid of me," coaxed the fox in a persuading tone. "All I want is an opportunity to gain your friendship. Why, I journeyed here this morning just on your account. I knew both your father and mother well, and I entertained them for dinner in my home."

The old fox chuckled to himself as he made this remark, for he remembered with great satisfaction what had occurred at that same dinner. Chanticleer's parents had made him a tasty meal, and he was sure their plump son would satisfy his appetite equally well.

"Your father had the finest voice I ever heard," went on the fox. "He used to stand on tiptoe, stretch out his neck, and crow with his eyes tight shut. I'm sure your voice equals your father's. I beg of you, dear Mr. Chanticleer, please do me the favor of letting me hear you crow."

Chanticleer was immensely flattered, and yielding to the suggestion of the crafty fox, he rose from the dust-wallow. Then he hopped up on the fence, stretched out his neck, shut his eyes, and began to crow.

Of course this was just the opportunity that the fox wanted. Before Chanticleer had finished crowing, the wily fox jumped into the air, grabbed Chanticleer by the neck, and slung him over his shoulder. Then off he started toward the woods at a great rate of speed.

Just then the hens spied the fleeing fox and began to cackle their loudest. The old woman came running out of the house to see what all the cackling was about.

"Alas! Alack!" she cried. "The fox has caught Chanticleer. Help! Help!"

Down the road ran the old woman, shrieking in alarm. The farmers stopped their labors and came to join the chase. A cow and her calf, three pigs, a cat, and a black dog accompanied them, mooing and grunting and meowing and barking.

Wasps and other insects swarmed overhead, buzzing as if in anger. And even the crows stopped eating the corn and set up a chorus of harsh caws. But it was useless.

The fleet fox outran them all. Then to confuse his pursuers, he ran straight into a flock of geese. And the frightened fowls ran hither and thither, hissing and squawking.

As poor Chanticleer looked about for an opportunity to escape, an idea came to him. Peering around the fox's snout he said in a meek voice, "Those silly people will never catch up with you at this rate. They should know better than to pursue a fox, for no creature is so fleet as you. Why don't you tell them to stop?"

The fox was quite flattered by the cock's praise. He acted on the suggestion at once and shouted at his pursuers.

The minute that the fox opened his mouth, Chanticleer fluttered his wings wildly and flew up on the limb of a tree and crowed:

"Cock-a-doodle-doo, cock-a-doodle-doo!
I know how to flatter, too!"

Then the fox realized he had been fooled by his own trick. From his pointed snout to the tip of his tail he was a picture of shame.

Chanticleer went home in triumph, but he promised himself never again to crow with his eyes shut or to be fooled by sly flattery.

# A Barber's Discovery

There once lived a village barber named Garo, who was a very fine barber, as everyone agreed. He was always willing to give a piece of advice, and he never ran out of things to say, as long as there was hair to cut or a beard that needed trimming.

In those days a barber traveled from house to house, like a peddler, to do his work. So Old Garo had a chance to observe just what was occurring, and for this reason his advice was considered excellent.

After a time people began to think that Garo had great wisdom, indeed, because he gave so much advice. And you may be sure that Garo himself agreed he had no equal.

One Sunday afternoon in late autumn he was taking a rest under an oak tree. His head leaned comfortably against the thick bark as he gazed at a nearby field where pumpkins lay yellow and fat in the sunshine. Garo observed that the fat pumpkins clung to slender green vines that wandered here and there like pieces of lost string.

Yawning drowsily the barber happened to glance up into the branches above his head. There hung hundreds of tiny brown acorns, ready to fall with the first harsh blast of winter wind.

Suddenly Garo wrinkled up his forehead. Then he began to squint his eyes and stroke his beard and twirl his thumbs the way he always did when he had made a discovery.

"Lo and behold!" he exclaimed in triumph. "Nature has made a big mistake! Observe these tiny acorns hanging on branches that are sturdy enough to bear the weight of an ox, while huge pumpkins grow on stringlike vines. How foolish! Even a simpleton knows that heavy pumpkins should grow on sturdy oaks and dainty acorns on slender vines."

Old Garo lay there, stroking his beard and squinting. How his customers would marvel when he told them of his discovery! "It's a pity I wasn't around when the world began," he said to himself. "I could have provided Nature with good advice." And so saying, the barber folded his hands over his fat stomach and fell into a deep slumber.

His stomach under his yellow shirt looked a great deal like one of those huge pumpkins. And his puffy brown nose didn't look very different from one of the acorns on the oak branches above his head.

Garo snored loudly in his slumber, just as he always did during his Sunday naps. As he snored, he smiled, too, because he was dreaming of his wonderful discovery.

All of a sudden an acorn was loosened by the wind. Down it dropped from a high branch and landed on the barber's nose with a loud plop, right in the middle of a snore.

Garo's snore turned to an angry snort as he caught a glimpse of the acorn that had plopped down on his nose, making it red and sore. Feeling his nose gently with fingers and thumb he stared at the acorn for a few minutes.

At last he shrugged. Then, still rubbing his sore nose thoughtfully with his thumb, he said meekly, "How foolish I was to even consider giving advice to Nature! And how sore my nose would be if that acorn had been a pumpkin! Nature is the best judge of what is good for the world." With that bit of solemn wisdom, he set out for home.

# The Seven Dancing Stars

A long, long time ago, when the world was young, a tribe of Indians dwelt in the midst of a forest. Suddenly one day all the wild creatures disappeared from the forest as if by magic. Not even the most skillful hunter could bring home meat for the cooking-pots.

The tribe roamed far and wide, seeking new hunting grounds, but wherever they went, the animals vanished.

At last Chief Big Hawk called his tribe together and related to them briefly what the Great Spirit had revealed to him.

"The Great Spirit bids us follow the setting sun," Big Hawk said. "Beyond towering cliffs is a lake which is the home of many beavers. There we shall find fish that leap into nets as eagerly as bees seek flowers. Bear and deer grow fat in the forest, and our cooking-pots will never be empty."

So once more the squaws gathered together their few belongings, and the next morning at daybreak the tribe started for the new hunting grounds.

When at last they reached the shores of the lake where the Great Spirit had led them, Big Hawk stopped and raised his right hand to the setting sun.

"Let us give thanks," he said in his deep, earnest voice. "Thank the Great Spirit who has aided us on our journey. May He be with us as we build our wigwams, and may He give us good hunting and years of peace."

So the Indians gave thanks to the Great Spirit and dwelt in their wigwams beside the lake. Meat was so plentiful that even an old squaw would not have returned from the woods empty-handed.

As the weather grew colder, the squaws of the tribe were as busy as the beavers, preparing food to last through the coming winter. So the children were often left to seek their own amusement.

One day Little Eagle, the eldest son of Chief Big Hawk, went with his seven brothers deep into the forest. There they came to an open circle, where the ground was as smooth and level as if it had been trampled by a thousand stamping feet. Giving no thought as to how such an open place happened to be in the midst of a thick forest, the children began a joyous dance.

Day after day they returned to dance in the mysterious circle, telling no one about it. One day as they danced, they heard a voice call out, "Beware! Beware! Strange things happen in this enchanted place."

Turning quickly they beheld a tall, stern-looking figure. The stranger was dressed in a robe of white feathers, and his long hair shone like silver. "Leave this place," he solemnly warned the children. "Remember my words and never return."

The children paid little or no heed to the stranger's solemn warning but went merrily on with their dancing.

"Let us bring food tomorrow," suggested Little Eagle, who was always ready to eat. "Then we can feast as well as dance."

His seven brothers agreed. But when they asked their mother for the food, she seemed vexed and refused to prepare it. "Eat in the wigwam as you should," she said.

So the brothers had to do without their feast, but they went to the circle to dance as before. All of a sudden a strange thing came to pass. The startled children found themselves rising into the air—up, up.

Their mother came out of the wigwam and saw them mounting into the sky. The squaw pleaded with them to return, promising them whatever food they desired.

Hearing his mother's words Little Eagle glanced toward the earth. Instantly there was a blinding flash, and Little Eagle was turned into a falling star! Down to earth he plunged in a streak of light.

But his seven brothers did not look back. They all reached the sky and became stars. There they still shine and twinkle to this day, a band of seven dancing children.

# Rumplestiltskin

## A Spinner of Gold

Once upon a time there was a poor miller who had a beautiful daughter. He loved her dearly and was so proud of her that he could never keep from bragging about her. One day a stranger came to the mill with a sack of corn to be ground into meal, and he saw the dainty lass in the doorway. As he beheld her lovely face, he said with envy, "I wish I had a daughter as beautiful as she."

The miller rubbed his mealy hands together and glanced at her standing there in the sunshine. He observed how the rays of the sun made her yellow hair glisten like gold, and he began to brag again.

"Yes, I consider her a lass in a thousand. She can spin straw into gold."

The man marveled at this tale, and he spread the news far and wide. At last it reached the ears of the King, who promptly sent word to the miller, bidding him come to the palace and fetch his daughter with him. So the miller obeyed at once.

"I have heard," said the King, "that this maid can spin straw into gold, and she must show if this be true. However, if she fails, beware, for you shall be punished."

The miller was so shaken with terror that his tongue stuck in his throat, and he dared not tell the truth about his careless boast.

Then the King led the lass into a stable, in which a spinning wheel and bundles of straw had been placed. He looked at her and smiled. "There," said he, "you have straw enough. Spin that into gold before morning." He withdrew quickly and locked the door.

The lass looked at the spinning wheel, and she looked at the straw. Then, thinking of the punishment her father would receive on the next day, she sank down on a bench and wept aloud. In the midst of her sobs she heard a slight rustle. From underneath the straw popped a brownie-like man with a peaked hat on his head. He had a brown withered face, a long red nose, and a rusty-red beard that swept down below his belt.

"Why all this fuss?" he asked harshly, regarding the maiden with piercing eyes.

The miller's daughter was so surprised at the sight of this mere wisp of a man that she stopped crying and told him the truth.

The dwarf twirled on his toes and laughed. "Spin straw into gold! That's no trouble. What will you give in payment if I spin it?"

The maid gazed at the dwarf in wonder. She had never before seen so odd and ugly a man. But his needle-sharp eyes had such cunning that she half-suspected he could do what he said. So she promised to give him her necklace.

On hearing that, the tiny dwarf flicked his fingers in the air, sat astride a three-legged milking stool in front of the spinning wheel, and began to spin.

Whir, whirr, whirrr! The straw seemed to fly through the air as if caught up in a gale. And in a moment, behold! All the straw was spun into glistening gold thread.

The little, long-nosed goblin got up from his stool. Then, accepting the necklace, he poked it into a pouch, and off he went.

Next morning when the King saw the thread, all of pure gold, he was extremely pleased. But his greed for gold increased with every glance at the glistening yellow heap. "Well and fair," said he, "well and fair. But you shall have another trial."

Then once more he shut the poor lass in a stable, at least half of which was filled with straw. "When that is spun into gold," he said, "you shall have praise indeed. If you fail me, beware of terrible punishment."

In his heart the greedy King pitied the lass, although he said nothing about it. Turning on his heel he went out of the room, locked the door, and left her to herself.

The poor maid was now greatly distressed. Yesterday's straw had been only a handful compared with what she had to spin today. "Oh, if only that little, long-nosed goblin were here to assist me!" she moaned.

Sadly she sat down at the wheel and tried to spin. But the straw remained only straw. "Alas and alack! There is no hope for me," she thought. But, lo! To her great relief, the dwarf appeared once more.

"Ah-ha!" said he. "What's wrong now?"

And when she had told him, he combed his rusty-red beard with his bony fingers and asked, "What shall I have in payment this time if I spin for you?" Then she promised to give him the pearl ring on her finger.

Flinging his beard over his shoulder and snapping his fingers, the dwarf plopped himself down on the stool and began to spin.

Whir, whirr, whirrr went the wheel, and the straw turned into melted gold. Smaller and smaller grew the heap of straw. Before dawn it was all spun into gold. And the dwarf had vanished long before the King arrived.

The King marveled greatly at the sight, but even yet his greedy mind was not satisfied. So he said, "Well and fair! Only one more trial, my dear, and you shall toil no more."

Then he took her into a stable which was heaped to its roof with yellow straw.

"Spin that into gold," said the King, "and tomorrow you shall be Queen."

With a glance over his shoulder he went out, locked the door, and left her to herself.

The maid sat down and looked hopelessly at the immense heap of straw. "Ah, me," she said, "to spin all that into gold would require the efforts of a hundred long-nosed goblins."

"What, what, what!" cried a voice, and in an instant little Master Long-Nose appeared for the third time.

But this time the poor lass had nothing left to offer him for his work.

The dwarf stared at the poor trembling maid for a moment, and then he said, "Promise me your first child if you ever have one, and tomorrow you shall be Queen."

The lass could not conceal her amusement at the idea. So never even suspecting that she could ever be Queen, she solemnly gave the binding promise required of her.

Then the wily dwarf balanced himself on his toe, twirled around nine times, and sat down at the wheel, whistling a tune.

Whirr, whirr, whirrrr went the wheel like the buzzing of a swarm of bees about a hive.

All night the dwarf sat busily spinning the straw. A few minutes before the sun rose next morning, the barn was swept clean, and the straw was all spun into gold. Then the dwarf skipped away on his wispy legs.

The King kept his promise and made the miller's daughter his Queen. So she lived happily and in great comfort at the King's fine palace, and upon the birth of her child the young Queen's joy was beyond compare.

### The Dwarf's Return

Sometime after the birth of her child, the Queen's joyous life was changed. One day she sat in the orchard, playing happily with her daughter. Then all in a moment her happiness was changed to grief, for, behold! There in the orchard beside her stood the dwarf as if he had sprung out of the trunk of a crooked apple tree nearby.

The dwarf slyly regarded the baby. "Ah! A pretty thing!" he said. "And mine!"

Until now the Queen had forgotten the promise she had made him in her desperate trouble. She pleaded earnestly with him. "I will give you anything else you wish if only you will free me from my promise and let me keep my beloved child."

"Nay, nay!" he refused. "A princess is a princess, and a promise is a promise. But I'll make another bargain with you. You shall have three days and nine chances to guess my name. If at noon of the third day you have not yet guessed it, then the child shall be mine." And he disappeared just as mysteriously as he had come.

All night long the Queen lay wide-awake, with the lamp burning high, wondering what name the dwarf could possess. Next morning she went sadly to the orchard, and just at noon the dwarf appeared.

"Ah, Madam!" said he. "Now what is my name?" And she guessed the silliest names she could think of—Catalawampus, Bumpetyboomery.

But at each one the dwarf shook his head. Then the Queen said a third name that just came to her mind. "Nickerruckerubblegrubb."

The dwarf broke into a hoot of laughter. "Madam, that is not my name," he squeaked. And hippity-hop! Off he went.

At exactly noon next day the ugly dwarf appeared. This time the Queen guessed the three oddest names she could think of— Long-Nose, Little-Body, and Puckity.

At each name the dwarf jiggled about, clapping his hands with glee. "Nay, nay, Madam," he shouted. "One more day, three more guesses, and the child is mine."

## The Queen's Plan

The Queen went back to the palace and sent for a messenger who was sharp of hearing and as keen of eye as a hawk. She told him what the little dwarf looked like with his withered face, wispy legs, long nose, rusty beard, and his high peaked hat. Then she ordered the messenger to ride like the wind, hither and thither, in search of the dwarf and to find out his name.

"Learn his name," she said, "and immense wealth shall be yours. If you fail, then you may expect harsh punishment."

The messenger lingered not even a moment. Flinging himself into the saddle he rode away. All night he rode hither and thither on his fleet-footed mare. At last, just before daybreak, he found himself at a crossroads, where he stopped and looked about.

A little way beyond the crossroads the messenger could see a tiny hut. Before it burned a fire, and dancing round the fire was an ugly little elf with a withered face, wispy legs, a long nose, and a rusty-red beard that flowed down below his belt.

One glimpse of the ugly, troll-like man convinced the messenger that this was the very dwarf whom the Queen had sent him to find. He dismounted and crept near the fire.

The dwarf was singing a joyous tune as he danced by the flickering firelight.

"Today I build a fire and bake.
  Tomorrow the Queen's child I'll take.
  No other one is called the same,
  For Rumplestiltskin is my name."

The messenger, lurking behind a big tree, listened carefully so as to be certain of the long name the dwarf was saying.

Then, rejoicing beyond measure, he crept silently back to his horse. He had barely sprung to his saddle when his steed lunged forward. Madly he raced to the palace to tell his news to the Queen.

The Queen was seated on her throne, speaking to the people of her royal court, when the messenger arrived. He knelt at her feet, whispering the name he had heard, and the Queen was almost overcome with joy.

After that she dressed in her finest satin robe and velvet cloak and went out to the orchard to await the arrival of the dwarf. A lady of the royal court carried the baby Princess in her arms as if she were quite ready to give her to the dwarf.

At the stroke of noon the horrible little goblin popped out as usual from behind the mossy old apple tree. This time he wore a peacock's feather in his hat. Over his arm was a lace-trimmed blanket he had fetched to wrap about the baby.

"Ah-ha!" he said. "Three more guesses, Madam, and the Princess is mine."

The Queen pleaded with him, promising him any treasure except her darling child. But the enraged dwarf refused in violent anger, and he snarled:

"A bargain's a bargain. A vow's a vow
   To the last word of it. Answer me now."

The Queen smiled to herself, and first she guessed, "Wheat-Straw."

The dwarf laughed in scornful amusement.

Next she guessed, "Heaps of Gold."

The dwarf laughed louder. And then the Queen smiled gleefully as she beckoned for the tiny dwarf to come closer. "How about Rumplestiltskin?" she murmured.

The dwarf stared at her as if in a wink he had been turned to stone. Then he trembled all over with rage and disappointment as he screamed, "The witches have told you my name! The witches have told you!"

He stamped on the ground so hard that one thin leg pierced the earth and sank into it up to the knee. Try as he might, he could not draw it out. In his fury Rumplestiltskin grasped his other leg, trying to pull himself free. He jerked with such force that he almost split himself in two. But he never pulled himself out.

# The Ugly Duckling

## Mother Duck's Queer Baby

It was midsummer. The air was fragrant with the mingled scent of clover and other flowers that grew in a meadow. In the midst of the meadow was a deep blue lake.

Among some slender reeds near the water's edge was a duck on her nest, and now her eggs were beginning to crack open.

"Cheep! Cheep! Cheep! Cheep!" One after another the ducklings came to life and began to poke out their heads.

"Quack! Quack!" said their admiring mother, and the ducklings tried to quack, too, as they ran hither and thither, peering

all about them at the beautiful green world. Their mother let them look as much as they liked, because green is good for the eyes.

"How big the world is!" they all said.

"Don't think this is the whole world," the mother duck told them. "It stretches a long, long way beyond this farm. Though I must say I've never been to the end of it myself.

"I hope you're all here," she continued, as she lifted herself off the nest to see if all the eggs had hatched. But the biggest egg had not hatched yet.

"Well, well," sighed Mother Duck. "I have never known an egg to take so long." And she settled herself on the nest again.

"Well, how are you getting on?" called an old duck, who had come for a friendly chat.

"This last egg is taking such a long time!" replied Mother Duck. "The shell will not crack open."

"Let me see the egg that will not hatch," said the old duck. "It may be a turkey's egg. The farmer's wife put one in my nest once, and what trouble I had when it hatched! The creature was afraid he'd drown and wouldn't go near the water.

"Yes, that's a turkey's egg," she added as Mother Duck raised up from the nest. "Leave it and teach the ducklings to swim."

"Oh, I'll be patient and sit on it a little longer," replied Mother Duck.

"Well," said the old duck as she waddled away. "I won't quarrel with you. I gave my advice only because of our long friendship."

At last the big egg cracked. "Cheep!" said the young one as he tumbled out of the shell. Mercy, how big and ugly he was!

"What a huge duckling!" said his mother. "None of the others looked like that. Can he be a turkey chick? Well, we shall soon find out. Into the water he shall go, if I have to push him into it myself."

The next day was gloriously fine, and the mother duck took her family to swim.

Splash! Into the water she plopped.

"Quack, quack," she called loudly, and one duckling after the other jumped in. The water dashed over their heads, but they came up to the surface again and floated properly. Their legs seemed to go of themselves quite naturally, and there they were, swimming about. Even the ugly gray one had sprung in eagerly and was swimming as well as the rest.

"Well, that is no turkey, at any rate," said Mother Duck in relief. "See how beautifully he uses his legs and how straight he holds himself. He is my own child after all."

Then she called to the ducklings, "Come with me, and I will take you into the world and introduce you to the duck yard. Keep close to me and beware of the cat."

Off she started, giving advice to the brood toddling along behind her.

"Remember to quack properly," said she. "Don't turn your toes in! Well-behaved ducklings turn their toes out, just as I do. Now bend your necks and say quack."

At the duck yard the ducklings all did as they were told. But when the other fowls saw the ugly one, they hissed at him and said, "Ugh, ugh! What a frightful object that gray one is!" Then a drake rushed at the poor creature and nipped him on the neck.

"Let him alone," said the mother. "He's not bothering you."

"I know," said the drake. "But he is so ugly. It's a pity he can't be made over. He's quite useless and not fit to be here."

"His looks will improve as he grows older," said his mother. "He was in the egg too long. That's why he isn't properly shaped."

But the duckling's looks did not improve, and he had a miserable time of it. The ducks pecked him till he was sore all over. Even his brothers and sisters found fault with him, until the poor creature could endure it no longer. At the first opportunity he dashed through the hedge and escaped from them all.

### The Search for a Home and Friends

The ugly duckling wandered about until he came to a tumble-down hut near the edge of a swamp. It was autumn now, and the wind whistled fiercely around the poor, ugly bird. He saw that the door was half open, and he ventured inside without permission.

An old woman dwelt there with her cat and her hen. "Meow," said the cat in a scornful manner. "What do you want?"

"Just a place for shelter from the wind's cold blasts," said the duckling meekly.

"Can you lay eggs?" demanded the hen.

"No! I can't lay eggs."

"Can you purr?" asked the cat.

"No!  I can't purr," replied the duckling.

"Well, if you can't lay eggs or purr, what can you do?" asked the hen, convinced that the duckling was hopelessly stupid.

"I can swim and dive," said the duckling.

"Swim and dive!" cried the cat and hen in amusement.  "Who cares to swim and dive? This is not the proper place for anyone who won't take the trouble to learn to lay eggs or to purr.  Go away, you useless beggar!"

So the duckling departed and stayed in the reeds near a lake where the wild ducks lived. But he was so ugly that he frightened them away.  After that he was always alone.

Winter set in.  Twirling dry leaves filled the air, icy blasts howled, and dark clouds, heavy with snow and sleet, coasted across the sky.  One dismal day, just at sunset, some enormous birds rose out of the reeds.

They were swans, and the duckling had never before seen anything like them. They were dazzlingly white with long, gracefully curved necks. Uttering strange cries, they spread their wings and flew southward, away from the region of sleet and snow.

As the swans circled in the air above him, the duckling circled round and round in the water to watch them. He stretched his neck to watch their flight. Then a curious sadness came over him, and he uttered a cry so loud and strange that it frightened him.

Soon the dreary winter days grew bitterly cold, and the duckling had to keep swimming to prevent the water from freezing around him. He paddled faster and faster, but at last he was so tired that he lay quite still, and soon he was a prisoner in solid ice.

Early the next morning a farmer found the helpless duckling. The man broke the ice and carried the bird home. There in the warmth of the kitchen the duckling began to stir about. The children made a fuss over him, wanting to pet him, but the duckling was afraid and sought to escape from them.

Plop! He landed right in the milk pail, spilling milk over the floor. Then he upset a tub of butter. Next he dived into the flour.

The two children pursued him, laughing and shouting. Their mother shrieked and lashed at him with the broom. At last the poor bird managed to flutter out the door and creep off. And for the rest of the winter he lurked in the midst of a swamp, without the friendship of any living creature.

In the spring when the sun began to shine warmly, the duckling found himself by a lake. Robins and wrens were singing joyously, and tiny green leaves were on the trees. The dazzling sunshine filled the duckling with such joy that he spread his wings wide.

They had grown stronger now, and to his surprise they carried him up into the air.

Up, up he soared, and before he knew it, he found himself above a large garden where apple trees stood in full blossom. Lilacs dropped their fragrant purple flowers into a glistening pool, and mingling flower scents filled the air with a glorious sweetness.

Suddenly from under the drooping bushes beside the pool three dazzlingly white swans came swimming. They ruffled their feathers and floated lightly over the water. As the duckling recognized the birds, the same sadness came over him again. He felt he had no choice but to go to them, even if they pecked him to death.

Down he flew and swam toward the swans. They floated out to meet him, their white feathers rustling. The poor duckling bowed his head, ready to endure any punishment, however harsh it might be.

Then he saw himself in the water, and, lo! He was no longer a gray bird, awkward and ugly. He himself was a swan!

Now he was glad for all his trouble, since it had finally brought him good fortune. The other swans stroked him lovingly with their beaks. Then some children came running. "Look," they cried, "there is a new swan! He is much handsomer than the others."

The young swan held his graceful head aloft, and his heart beat joyously as he exclaimed, "I never dreamed of so much happiness when I was an ugly duckling!"

# The Golden Eggs

Long and long ago a peasant man and his good wife dwelt in a humble cottage beside a winding stream. The happy couple lacked many things that their richer neighbors enjoyed, but they were always willing to share what they had.

No matter how little they had themselves, they always put out a bit of food for the wild creatures that came to the stream to drink. The good wife never neglected to toss a handful of crumbs to the robins and wrens and to scatter grain on the riverbank for the wild fowls.

One day a splendid wild goose flew down to the farmyard and made herself at home. She did not fly off again, but settled down in a dust-wallow with the hens.

Next morning when the wife heard the hens cackling, she went out to get the eggs. She saw the wild goose fly off a nest flapping her wings and looking extremely wise.

"Oho!" exclaimed the woman. "A goose egg! It will fetch a good price."

She ran to the nest, and there in a hollow of hay lay an egg of solid gold! The woman was so excited that she began screaming for her husband, who was spading a bean patch.

"G-G-G-Goose! S-S-S-Solid gold egg," she stuttered breathlessly.

"Have the fairies bewitched your tongue?" he asked. "What are you stuttering about?"

"Oh, husband," the woman began again, trying to speak more calmly. "The wild goose has just laid an egg of solid gold."

"Solid gold!" cried the man. "Where?"

"I-I-In the barn," she stuttered.

"Simpleton!" shrieked her excited husband. "Do you lack a mind to think with? Why did you leave a solid gold egg in the barn, where a common thief might steal it?"

He rushed into the barn and picked up the golden egg. How it glittered in the sunlight! The man was nearly overcome with rapture.

"We must conceal this rare treasure," he said, "or someone will surely steal it."

So they selected a hiding place under the clay bricks in the hearth and sat down to marvel at their good fortune. They thought about the precious egg all day, neglecting their work and forgetting to feed their few chickens and the wild creatures. When night came, they could not sleep a wink for wondering if they would find another golden egg the following day.

Next morning they were up before dawn. Carrying a lamp, they rushed to the barn. There in a nest lay a second glittering egg of solid gold. The couple's rapture knew no bounds as they regarded the treasure with wondering eyes.

417

Day after day the goose laid a golden egg. Day after day the greedy partners buried the egg and loitered in the house to guard the treasure. They neglected their work and forgot that the chickens and wild fowls lacked food. They were completely bewitched by dazzling dreams of rare wealth.

"I shall soon be the wealthiest man in the land," boasted the peasant. Then hooking his thumbs over his belt, he tried to reckon the worth of his treasure and to decide what it would buy—choice food, handsome horses, a carriage, and anything else he chose. But suddenly he felt that he could not endure waiting another instant for his great riches.

"I'll cut the goose open and get all her eggs at once," he cried. So he rushed out and killed the goose. Cutting her open, he found her—like any common goose!

"Alas and alack!" he cried in despair. "Why did I kill the goose that laid the golden eggs? If I hadn't been so greedy, I could have improved my good fortune. At least I've learned a lesson. Things worth having are worth waiting for."

# Cinder Lad

## The Mystery of the Hayfield

Once on a time there was a man who had a meadow which he prized very highly for its fine hay. But right on Midsummer's Eve, when the grass stood thickest and greenest, the meadow was suddenly eaten down to the ground as if a whole flock of sheep had been grazing on it overnight.

When this occurred a second year, the man felt he could not endure having his fine crop ruined again. So the third year he told his sons that one of them must stay in the barn on Midsummer's Eve to watch the hay.

So the eldest son set off to the barn and lay down to sleep. Suddenly there came the sound of booming thunder, and the very planks on the floor rattled as if there were an earthquake. Up jumped the lad and took to his heels nor dared to look around till he got home. So the hay disappeared again on Midsummer's Eve as it had done before.

Next year when Midsummer's Eve came, the next eldest son went to guard the meadow.

Again there came the booming thunder. The lad took to his heels as if bewitched, and the hay was destroyed as before.

Next year the turn came to Cinder Lad, the youngest son, but when he made ready to go, his brothers laughed sneeringly and said, "A fine guard you'll make! All you've ever done is to sit on a bench among the cinders and twirl your thumbs."

In spite of the teasing, Cinder Lad did not despair, and he proceeded to the barn. Soon the barn began to creak and quake.

"Well," said the boy, "if it doesn't get any worse than this, I can stand it."

But the uproar grew worse and still worse. Suddenly it ceased, and the air was as still as death. Instead of fleeing, Cinder Lad tiptoed across the barn and peeked over the top of the half-open door.

There stood a spanking big horse, eating away as if he would never stop. One glance convinced the lad that this was no common steed, for by his side lay a plumed helmet, a sword, and a full suit of massive armor for a knight, all made of glittering brass.

"Ah!" said the lad. "So it's you who eats our hay. Well, I'll attend to you." And he proceeded to conceal both horse and armor in a secret place without further waiting.

When Cinder Lad got home, his father and brothers questioned him closely. But instead of relating his true adventures, he merely claimed that he had not heard anything to be afraid of. The brothers suspected that he was not telling the whole truth, but there was the meadow as thick and green as before.

The next year when Midsummer's Eve came, the two elder brothers again lacked the courage to watch the hay. So Cinder Lad set out to the barn, and a storm arose as before. But compared to these terrific blasts, last year's uproar had been a mere whisper.

Suddenly the air was still, and Cinder Lad looked out. There stood another giant horse, munching away at a great rate. He was far handsomer than the horse which had come the year before and of a size rarely seen. By his side was a full suit of armor for a knight, all made of silver.

"Ah!" said the lad. "So it's you who eats up our hay. I'll attend to you." He led this horse to the place where he had concealed the other and then returned to his home.

"Well," said one of his brothers sneeringly, "I suppose you'll claim there's no damage to our hayfield."

"That I do!" declared Cinder Lad, showing no further concern in the matter.

But the others, suspecting his word, ran off to see the meadow. Lo and behold! There stood the hay, thicker and greener than ever.

The next year the two elder brothers still were afraid. So Cinder Lad was required to watch the field. Again came the peals of thunder and then the great silence.

When the brave lad looked out, he saw a horse, far finer and fatter than the others. Beside him lay armor of purest gold.

Cinder Lad proceeded to hide the horse and went to report that the hay was safe.

## The Trials at the Glass Hill

The King of the country where Cinder Lad lived had a daughter who was beautiful beyond compare. The King proclaimed that this Princess should marry only a man who could ride up a steep glass hill which was as smooth and slippery as ice.

The King further proclaimed that the Princess would sit at the top of the hill with three golden apples in her lap. Whoever could ride up the slippery hill and carry off the golden apples was to claim the Princess for his bride and half the kingdom besides. Everyone in the entire realm was invited to attend the trials at the glass hill.

Knights and princes from all the realm accepted the King's invitation, and naturally everyone came to watch the rare sight. The two elder brothers set off to the trials, but they sneeringly refused to let Cinder Lad accompany them.

All day long the gallant noblemen sought to conquer the hill, but no one could proceed even so far as twice the length of his horse.

The King was about to proclaim that no further trials would be held until next day, when up came a knight dressed in glittering brass armor. He charged up the hill at full speed, sparks flying from the forefeet of his splendid horse. Up he went about a third of the way.

When the Princess beheld the knight in the brass armor, she wished that he might claim her for his wife. But the horse came a third of the way and no farther. Then back he slipped. Quickly the Princess tossed one of her golden apples after the strange knight, flinging it right into his lap.

When the knight reached the foot of the hill, he galloped off before anyone could prevent his disappearance.

Next day the two brothers, neglecting their work as before, set off to attend the trial. Cinder Lad pleaded to go along with them, but they would have none of him.

Once again the knights and princes tried to urge their horses up the hill. They rode and slipped and slipped and rode, but there was not one who could force his panting steed up the hill.

All at once a knight dressed in silver armor came riding into the midst of the watching throng, astride a black horse of uncommon size. Straight toward the hill he charged and rode directly up until he had gone two-thirds of the way.

Suddenly the black horse wheeled with his forefeet in the air to start down again.

The Princess gazed with rapture at the gallant rider. Before he had turned around, she had sprung to her feet and thrown the second apple to him. But as soon as the knight reached the foot of the hill, he rode off so fast that no one knew where he went.

On the third day everything occurred as it had on the two days before. Cinder Lad again begged to go, but his brothers would not give him permission to accompany them.

For the third time the knights urged their horses up the hill, but no one could improve on his attempt of the day before. No one got farther than a quarter of the way up.

At last a knight came riding on a horse so huge that no one had ever seen its equal. This mysterious knight wore a suit made of golden armor, so bright that the sunbeams gleamed from it a mile off.

Up the hill he went at full speed, took the third apple from the Princess in triumph, and then he rode down the hill and away before anyone could halt his fleet steed.

Now when the brothers got home that evening, they related the wonderful deed of the knight in golden armor, and Cinder Lad listened as if bewitched by the tale.

"Such glorious armor has never been seen in the whole kingdom or even in the whole world," they boasted with sighs of rapture.

"I-I," stuttered Cinder Lad, "I wish I could have seen him!"

"You!" sneered the eldest brother. "Why the knight wouldn't have even glanced at a stuttering simpleton like you."

Next day the King's messenger sought out all the knights and bade them come to the palace. Then the one who could show the golden apples might claim the Princess.

Up to the palace they all came, one after the other, but not a single one possessed a golden apple. And not one could explain the disappearance of the mysterious knight.

"Alas! Alack!" cried the King in despair. "Where is the champion in golden armor?"

Then the King proclaimed that everyone in the whole kingdom—young or old, rich or poor—should be sought out and brought to the palace. So to the palace they all came— knights and ladies, cooks, carpenters, inn- keepers, bootblacks, and serving-maids. But no one had seen the golden apples. No one knew who the golden knight might be, for his armor had covered him from head to toe. Therefore no one had caught even a glimpse of his face.

The two brothers of Cinder Lad were the last ones in the whole realm to come to the palace to be questioned, but of course they knew nothing of the golden apples.

"Is there no one else in all my kingdom?" asked the despairing King. "I am requiring every subject to come before me."

"Oh," said the eldest brother, "there's our young brother, but he could not have seen the golden apples. I'm sure he hasn't left his chimney corner for the last three days."

"Never mind that," said the King. "Fetch him to me."

So the brothers ran home at once to fetch Cinder Lad and dragged him to the palace, dressed just as he was in a ragged old cloak.

"Speak out, lad," ordered the King when Cinder Lad came to the foot of the throne. "Do you have the golden apples?"

"Yes, sir," answered Cinder Lad. "Here is the first, and here is the second, and here is the third one, too."

Then flinging off his ragged old cloak, the lad stood before the King dressed in glorious golden armor.

"Ah!" cried the King, embracing him. "You shall wed my daughter and rule the western half of my realm. So gallant a knight well deserves a rich reward."

# BOOKS TO READ

Here are the names of good books that provide more of the same fun and adventure we find in *Times and Places*.

## Young Citizens of Today

*Understood Betsy*.   Dorothy Canfield Fisher.
*Jory's Cove*.   Clara Bice.
*A Name for Obed*.   Ethel Calvert Phillips.
*The Sea Is All Around*.   Elizabeth Enright.
*Augustus and the River*.   Le Grand Henderson.
*Brownie of the Circus*.   Wilhelmina Harper.
*Greased Lightning*.   Sterling North.
*Skookum and Sandy*.   Richard Bennett.
*Americans Every One*.   Lavinia Davis.
*A Tree for Peter*.   Kate Seredy.
*A Boy Named John*.   John Cournos.
*Democracy*.   Omar and Ryllis Goslin.
*Sarah's Idea*.   Doris Gates.
*Storm on the Island*.   Eleanor Lattimore.
*Debby*.   Siddie Joe Johnson.
*Cindy*.   Dorothy Aldis.
*The Moffats*.   Eleanor Estes.
*Alice-All-by-Herself*.   Elizabeth Coatsworth.
*A House for Elizabeth*.   Dean Marshall.
*Houseboat Summer*.   Elizabeth Coatsworth.
*Steady*.   James and Marion Renick.

## Young Citizens of Early Days

*By Wagon and Flatboat*.   Enid Meadowcroft.
*Dancing Tom*.   Elizabeth Coatsworth.
*The Treasure in the Little Trunk*.   Helen F. Orton.
*Wind in the Chimney*.   Cornelia Meigs.
*The Little House in the Big Woods*.   Laura Wilder.
*Little Grey Gown*.   Mabel Hunt.
*Skippack School*.   Marguerite de Angeli.
*A Story of Pioneers and Their Children*.   Myers and Embree.

*Young Settler.*   Phil Stong.
*The Matchlock Gun.*   Walter Edmonds.
*Abraham Lincoln.*   Ingri and Edgar d'Aulaire.
*Abe Lincoln's Other Mother.*   Bernadine Bailey.
*Homespun Playdays.*   Caroline Bailey.
*Abigail.*   Sperry and Donaldson.
*Susannah, the Pioneer Cow.*   Miriam Mason.
*Smiling Hill Farm.*   Miriam Mason.
*Steamboat Billy.*   Sanford Tousey.
*Abe Lincoln, Frontier Boy.*   Augusta Stevenson.
*Children of the Handcrafts.*   Caroline Bailey.
*Katy's Quilt.*   Ruth Holbrook.
*The Little House on Wheels.*   Marjorie Hayes.
*"Hello, the Boat!"* Phyllis Crawford.
*Along the Erie Towpath.*   Enid Meadowcroft.
*How to Make Historic American Costumes.*   Mary Evans.

## Wonders of Our Times

*Gloucester Boy.*   Ruth and Richard Holberg.
*Coast Guard to Greenland.*   Anne Malloy.
*Famous Inventors for Boys and Girls.*   Irmengard Eberle.
*Make Way for the Mail.*   John J. Floherty.
*Grindstone Farm.*   Henry B. Lent.
*Flight of the Silver Bird.*   Ruth and Latrobe Carroll.
*Diggers and Builders.*   Henry B. Lent.
*Clear Track Ahead.*   Henry B. Lent.
*Sky High.*   E. T. Hurd.
*Time Was.*   Hildegard Woodward.
*Mr. Pink and the House on the Roof.*   Edith Heal.
*Mike Mulligan and His Steam Shovel.*   Virginia Burton.
*A Steam Shovel for Me!*   Vera Edelstadt.
*Father's Big Improvements.*   Caroline Emerson.
*The Travels of Mr. Trot.*   Elsie Hart.
*The Trailer Book.*   W. C. Pryor.
*Portraits of the Iron Horse.*   R. S. Henry.
*World's Messengers.*   H. H. Webster.
*Man Conquers the World with Science.*   W. L. Nida.

*Engine, Engine Number Nine.*   E. T. Hurd.
*Automobiles from Start to Finish.*   Franklin Reck.
*Power from Start to Finish.*   Franklin and Claire Reck.
*The Book of Modern Airplanes.*   Harold Booth.
*Hezekiah Horton.*   Ellen Tarry.
*High Up in a Penthouse.*   Virginia Andrews.
*The New Alphabet of Aviation.*   E. Shenton.

## Story-Land of Here and Now

*Just for Fun.*   Robert Lawson.
*Rootabaga Stories and Rootabaga Pigeons.*   Carl Sandburg.
*The Rainbow Cat and Other Stories.*   Rose Fyleman.
*Mr. Popper's Penguins.*   Richard and Florence Atwater.
*Peterkin Papers.*   Lucretia P. Hale.
*The Story of Dr. Dolittle.*   Hugh Lofting.
*The Voyages of Dr. Dolittle.*   Hugh Lofting.
*Winnie-the-Pooh.*   A. A. Milne.
*Adventures of Pinocchio.*   Collodi.
*Just So Stories.*   Rudyard Kipling.
*Mary Poppins and Mary Poppins Comes Back.*   P. L. Travers.
*Felicia the Curious Cow.*   J. Dewitt.
*Andy and the Lion.*   James Daugherty.
*Princess September and the Nightingale.*   Somerset Maugham.
*Story of Ferdinand.*   Munro Leaf.
*The King's Stilts.*   Dr. Seuss.
*Don't Blame Me.*   Richard Hughes.
*The Adventures of Dudley and Gilderoy.*   Algernon Blackwood.
*Whistle for Good Fortune.*   Margery Bailey.
*Peter Pan.*   James M. Barrie.
*The Wizard of Oz.*   Frank L. Baum.
*To and Again.*   Walter Brooks.
*Elizabite.*   H. A. Rey.
*The Rabbits' Revenge.*   Kurt Wiese.
*Black, White, and Caroline.*   Susan Ertz.
*The Sorcerer's Apprentice.*   Richard Rostron.

# Young Citizens of Other Lands

*The Village That Learned to Read.* Elizabeth Tarshis.
*Children of the Fiery Mountain.* Marian Cannon.
*Mario and the Chuna.* Esther Hall.
*Wings over South America.* Alice Dalgliesh.
*Panuck, Eskimo Sled Dog.* Frederick Machetanz.
*Panchita A Little Girl of Guatemala.* Delia Goetz.
*Jorge's Journey.* Alice C. Desmond.
*Spanish-American Song and Game Book.* Mexico Writers, Art, and Music Projects.
*Kanguk A Boy of Bering Strait.* William Albee.
*The Least One.* Ruth Sawyer.
*Manuela's Birthday in Old Mexico.* Laura Bannon.
*The Burro That Had a Name.* Lorraine and Jerrold Beim.
*Cedar Deer.* Addison Burbank.
*The Silver Llama.* Alida Malkus.
*Pablo of Flower Mountain.* Christine Von Hagen.
*The Lucky Llama.* Alice Desmond.
*Pablo's Pipes.* Frances Eliot.
*Pedro.* Flack and Larsson.
*The Forest Pool.* L. A. Armer.
*Two Children of Brazil.* Rose Brown.
*Nuvat the Brave.* Radko Doone.
*Tito, Pig of Guatemala.* C. E. Jackson.
*Maria Rosa.* Vera Kelsey.

# The Great Outdoors

*Bushy Tail.* Gall and Crew.
*Wild Animals I Have Known.* Ernest Thompson Seton.
*Polar Bear Twins.* Jane Tompkins.
*War Paint, an Indian Pony.* Paul Brown.
*Smoozie.* Alma Savage.
*Jud Goes Camping.* Bernard S. Mason.
*Plouf the Little Wild Duck.* Lida.
*Whisk.* David Stearns.
*Forestry Primer.* American Tree Association.
*Salute.* C. W. Anderson.

*My First Horse.*   Will James.

*The Blind Colt.*   Glen Rounds.

*Joan and the Three Deer.*   Marjorie Medary.

*Bambi.*   Felix Salten.

*Sharp Ears the Baby Whale.*   John Beaty.

*The Tale of the Whitefoot Mouse.*   Henry Kane.

*Honk the Moose.*   Phil Stong.

*Where Did Your Garden Grow?*   J. L. Lucas.

*Real Boys and Girls Go Birding.*   Jack Van Coevering.

*From Robin to Junco.*   Mary I. Curtis.

*Fire the Mascot.*   Paul Brown.

*The Restless Robin.*   Marjorie Flack.

*War Horse.*   Paul Brown.

*Make Way for the Ducklings.*   Robert McCloskey.

*Blinky.*   Agnes Akin Atkinson.

*Wild Animal Pets.*   W. L. Finlay.

*Sajo and the Beaver People.*   Grey Owl.

*My Friend Flicka.*   Mary O'Hara.

*Prairie Neighbors.*   Patch and Fenton.

*Animals of North American History.*   Paul Bransom.


## Famous People of Long Ago

*Junior Bible.*   E. J. Goodspeed.

*Stories from the Old Testament.*   Maud and Miska Petersham.

*Once Upon A Time in Egypt.*   Frances Gere.

*David.*   E. O. Jones.

*Joseph.*   F. W. Klaber.

*Saint George and the Dragon.*   Alice Dalgliesh.

*Joan of Arc.*   Louis Boutet de Monvel.

*Bible Stories to Read and Tell.*   Frances Olcott.

*Joseph Haydn: The Merry Little Peasant.*   Deucher and Wheeler.

*Giotto Tended the Sheep.*   Deucher and Wheeler.

*Through Golden Windows.*   Mary Reely.

*The Boyhood Adventures of Our Presidents.*   Frances Cavanah.

*Ben Franklin, Printer's Boy.*   Augusta Stevenson.

*Benjamin Franklin.*   Enid Meadowcroft.

*David Farragut, Midshipman.* R. N. Chavanne.
*A Treasury of Heroes and Heroines.* Edwards.
*Bible Children.* Blanche J. Thompson.
*Saint George of England.* Basil Hood.

## Old Tales from Everywhere

*Fables of La Fontaine.* Margaret Wise Brown.
*Rufus the Fox.* Samivel (Margery Bianco).
*Book of Fables and Folk Stories.* H. E. Scudder.
*Red Indian Fairy Book.* F. J. Olcott.
*The Talking Stone.* Caroline Cunningham.
*Tales from Grimm.* Wanda Gág.
*Clever and Foolish Tales for Children.* Maude O. Walters.
*Stars, Their Facts and Legends.* F. A. Grondal.
*Household Stories.* Jacob and Wilhelm Grimm (Lucy Crane).
*It's Perfectly True.* H. C. Andersen (Paul Leyssac).
*Fables of Aesop.* Joseph Jacobs.
*East of the Sun and West of the Moon.* Peter Asbjornsen.
*Molly Whuppie.* Joseph Jacobs.
*The Old Man Is Always Right.* H. C. Andersen.
*Old Peter's Russian Tales.* Arthur Ransome.
*Tales from a Finnish Tupa.* J. C. Bowman.
*Happily Ever After.* Alice Dalgliesh.
*Stories That Never Grow Old.* Watty Piper.
*Three Sneezes.* Roger Duvoisin.
*Wonderful Adventures of Nils.* Selma Lagerlöf.
*The Little Mermaid.* H. C. Andersen.

# GLOSSARY

a ban′ don, 1. give up. 2. leave.

ac cept′, take what is offered.

ac com′ pa ny, go along with.

ac com′ plish, do; carry out.

ac cuse′, 1. charge with having done wrong. 2. find fault with; blame.

ac cus′ tomed, 1. usual. 2. **Accustomed to** means used to.

ad vance′, move forward; go on.

ad′ ver tise, give public notice of; announce.

a lert′, 1. watchful; wide-awake. 2. lively. 3. **On the alert** means watchful.

a maze′ ment, great surprise; sudden wonder.

am′ ble, go in a slow, easy way.

an noy′, tease; make angry.

ap par′ent ly, 1. seemingly. 2. clearly; plainly.

ap proach′, 1. come near or nearer. 2. act of coming near.

arc′ tic, 1. near the North Pole. 2. the region near the North Pole.

ar′ e a, 1. amount of surface. 2. region; part of the country.

ar′ mor, covering worn to protect the body when fighting.

a rouse′, 1. awaken. 2. excite; stir to action.

as sist′, help.

a stride′, with one leg on each side of. He sits astride a horse.

at tend′, 1. be present at. 2. take care of.

at ten′ dant, person who waits on another; a servant.

bade, commanded; ordered.

bal′ ance, 1. power to stand steadily. 2. make up for; even up. 3. steady. He was balanced on one toe.

bale, a large bundle securely tied with wire or twine; as, a bale of hay.

beck′ on, signal by motion of hand or head.

be held′, saw.

be ware′, be careful.

bid, command.

bind, 1. tie; tie together. 2. hold by promise.

blast, a strong sudden rush of wind or air.

bliz′ zard, a blinding snowstorm with strong wind and great cold.

bolt, 1. dash off; run away. 2. give a sudden start.

bound, 1. leap; jump. 2. limit. 3. going; on the way.

bril′ liant, very bright; shining; brightly colored.

brim, the part of a hat that shades the eyes.

brim′ ming, full to the top.

brood, a family of young birds.

brush′ wood, 1. small trees or bushes growing rather thickly together. 2. branches or bushes broken or cut off.

budge, move slightly.

cab, covered part of a steam shovel where the operator sits.

cac′ tus, a prickly plant without leaves that grows in hot, dry countries.

calm, 1. quiet; still; not stirred up. 2. quietness. 3. make quiet.

can′ yon, a narrow valley with steep sides.

cast, 1. throw; throw off. 2. throw a line to catch fish.

cau′ tious, very careful; never taking chances.

cease, stop.

chal′ lenge, dare to fight.

cham′ pi on, 1. person who fights for the rights of others. 2. defend. 3. winner.

**choice,** 1. a chance to choose. 2. excellent; of fine quality.

**cliff,** a high steep rock.

**clus′ter,** 1. a group or bunch. 2. be in a group; gather in a group.

**com mis′sion er,** person in charge of some public department, such as roads, police, etc.

**com mo′tion,** excitement; uproar; noisy moving about.

**com plete′,** 1. with all the parts; whole; entire. 2. finish.

**con ceal′,** hide.

**con cern′,** 1. worry. 2. interest.

**con cern′ing,** about.

**con fess′,** 1. admit; own up. 2. admit that you are guilty.

**con fuse′,** mix up.

**con′quer,** overcome; win over.

**con sent′,** 1. agree. 2. agreement.

**con sid′er,** 1. think about in order to decide. 2. think to be.

**con vince′,** persuade; make someone feel that something is true.

**cour′age,** bravery; meeting danger without fear.

**court′yard,** space enclosed by walls in or near a large building.

**craft′y,** clever at fooling others; sly.

**crib,** a building for storing grain.

**cud,** food brought back from the stomach of cows and some other animals for a second chewing.

**cu′ri ous,** 1. eager to know; wondering. 2. strange; odd; unusual.

**curt′sey,** bow or greeting of respect made by bending the knees and lowering the body slightly.

**dazed,** confused. He was so dazed by the blow on his head that he could not find his way home.

**daz′zle,** 1. hurt (the eyes) with too bright or with quick-moving lights. 2. overcome with something very bright.

**de fend′,** keep safe; protect.

**de ny′,** 1. say (something) is not true. 2. say that you do not believe.

**de spair′,** 1. loss of hope; dreadful feeling that nothing good can happen. 2. lose hope.

**des′per ate,** frightened; frantic.

**de vour′,** eat greedily.

**dif′fi cult,** not easy; hard to do or understand.

**dif′fi cul ty,** trouble.

**di rect′,** manage; guide; order.

**di rect′ly,** in a straight line; straight.

**dis guise′,** hide what you are by appearing as something else.

**dis′mal,** 1. dark; gloomy. 2. dreary; miserable; unpleasant.

**dis tress′,** great pain or sorrow; trouble; worry.

**dis turb′,** 1. break in upon with noise or change. 2. make uneasy; trouble; bother; annoy.

**doze,** 1. sleep lightly. 2. a light sleep; a nap.

**Dr.,** Doctor.

**dread,** 1. fear. 2. fearful; awful.

**drift′wood′,** wood washed ashore by the water.

**drowse,** sleep lightly.

**drow′sy,** sleepy; half asleep.

**dull,** 1. not sharp; not pointed. 2. not bright; not clear. 3. not interesting; not pleasant.

**ear′nest,** serious; strong and firm in purpose.

**earth′quake,** a shaking or sliding of the ground, caused by changes far beneath the surface.

**ef′fort,** 1. the use of strength to do something hard. 2. a hard try; strong attempt.

**el′der,** older.

**em brace′,** hug; hold in the arms.

**en chant′,** use magic on; put under a spell.

**en dure′,** bear. He could scarcely endure the pain.

**en′vy,** want something another person has.

**e′vil,** 1. bad; wicked. 2. wicked deed.

**ex plore′,** 1. travel over unknown land for the purpose of discovery. 2. examine carefully.

**ex treme′,** 1. very great; very strong; extremely. 2. much more than usual; very.

**faith′ful,** 1. loyal; true; as, a faithful friend.

**fal′ter,** 1. stop for a moment. 2. stumble.

**fam′ine,** 1. not enough food in a country. 2. a time when food is scarce.

**fee′bly,** weakly.

**fleet,** moving swiftly; rapid.

**fore′feet,** front feet.

**fore told′,** said would come true.

**for′tu nate,** lucky.

**fra′grant,** sweet-smelling.

**fran′ti cal ly,** with wild excitement.

**fre′quent,** 1. happening often. 2. near together. 3. happening every little while.

**fre′quent ly,** often.

**ful fill′,** make true.

**fu′ri ous,** very angry.

**fu′ry,** 1. great anger. 2. fierceness.

**gale,** a very strong wind.

**gal′lant,** brave.

**gan′der,** a male goose.

**glee,** joy; delight.

**glimpse,** 1. a short look. 2. catch a short look. 3. **Catch a glimpse** means get sight of.

**gloss′y,** smooth and shiny.

**gob′lin,** a mischievous elf in the form of an ugly little man.

**gourd,** 1. the fruit of a plant whose dried shell is sometimes used for bottles and bowls. 2. the plant itself.

**grad′u al,** little by little.

**grant,** 1. allow; give what is asked; as, to grant a request. 2. admit.

**graze,** feed on growing grass.

**guilt′y,** 1. to blame. The girl felt guilty. 2. knowing or showing that one has done wrong.

**gul′ly,** steep little valley; ditch.

**heed,** take notice of; obey.

**heif′er,** a young cow.

**hes′i tate,** 1. hold back; feel doubtful; be undecided; show that one has not made up one's mind. 2. stop an instant; pause. 3. speak in a hesitating way.

**hith′er,** 1. here; to this place. 2. on this side. **Hither and thither** means here and there.

**hum′ble,** not important; not grand.

**hus′tle,** 1. hurry. 2. push or shove roughly.

**i′dle,** 1. not busy. 2. lazy. 3. waste time. 4. go slowly.

**im mense′,** very great.

**in crease′,** 1. make greater, richer, or more powerful. 2. become greater; grow in size or number.

**in′jure,** do damage to; harm; hurt.

**in tent′ly,** closely. **Intent upon** means interested in.

**jun′gle,** wild land thickly overgrown with trees, bushes, and vines.

**king′dom,** the land ruled by one king.

**lash,** 1. tie or fasten with cord. 2. hit. 3. beat back and forth.

**ledge,** 1. narrow shelf. 2. a shelf of rock.

**lin′ger,** stay on; go slowly as if unwilling to leave.

**lo′cate,** find; discover.

**loi′ter,** walk slowly, stopping now and then; stop and play along the way.

**loy′al,** true to one's king or country.

**lunge,** 1. sudden forward movement. 2. move forward suddenly.

**lurk,** stay about without arousing attention; wait out of sight; be hidden.

**mare,** female horse.

**mar′vel,** wonder greatly.

**mass,** 1. lump. 2. large amount or number together.

**mas′sive,** large and heavy.

**mer′chant,** trader; person who buys and sells things to others.

**mere,** nothing else than; only.

**min′gle,** mix.

**mis′er a ble,** 1. unhappy. 2. causing trouble or unhappiness; as, a miserable cold. 3. poor; wretched

**mist,** 1. fog or cloud.

**moist,** slightly wet; damp.

**mut′ter,** 1. speak low and indistinctly with lips partly closed. 2. complain; grumble.

**neg lect′,** 1. leave undone. 2. fail.

**nes′tle,** settle comfortably.

**nick′er,** 1. a sound made by a horse. 2. make a nickering sound.

**nim′ble,** lively; quick moving; sure-footed.

**nudge,** 1. push lightly. 2. a slight push.

**ob serve′,** 1. see and notice; watch. 2. examine closely.

**oc ca′sion al,** happening once in awhile.

**oc cur′,** happen; take place.

**op por tu′ni ty,** good chance; favorable time.

**op′pos ite,** facing; across from.

**or′di nar y,** common; usual.

**pan′ic,** a wild, terrible fear.

**pause,** stop for a time.

**peas′ant,** 1. a poor farmer. 2. of a peasant.

**pe cul′iar,** strange; odd; unusual.

**pep′per,** 1. a seasoning with a hot taste. 2. a hollow red or green vegetable that is baked or fried. 3. sprinkle with pepper. 4. fly thick and fast.

**per mit′,** let; allow.

**per suade′,** make willing; cause to believe.

**pin′to,** a horse spotted in two colors.

**plan ta′tion,** a very large farm.

**pla′za,** a public square in a city or town.

**plead,** beg; ask for.

**pos sess′,** 1. own; have. 2. hold; occupy.

**pounce,** jump on suddenly and seize.

**pre fer′,** like better.

**pre vent′,** 1. keep from. 2. keep from happening.

**prey,** 1. animal hunted and seized for food. 2. hunt and seize for food.

**pro ceed′,** 1. go forward. 2. go.

**pro claim′,** announce; make known publicly.

**pro tec′tion,** 1. keeping safe from harm. 2. a thing or person that prevents harm. 3. shelter.

**prowl,** go about slowly and secretly, looking for something to eat or steal.

**pur′pose,** 1. plan; aim; something one has in mind to get or do. 2. **On purpose** means with a purpose, not by accident.

**pur′pose ly,** with a plan or aim; not by accident.

**pur sue′,** chase.

**pur su′er,** one who pursues.

**quake,** shake; tremble.

**rap′ture,** very great joy.

**rare,** unusual.

**ra′tion,** a certain allowance of food.

**realm,** kingdom.

**re cov′er,** 1. get back. 2. get better. 3. get over.

**reed,** a kind of tall grass that grows in wet places.

**re fuse′,** 1. be unwilling. 2. say "no." 3. say that one will not do something. 4. show by words or acts that one will not do something.

**re gard′,** look closely at.

**re late′,** tell; report.

**re lief′,** 1. freedom from pain, worry, or difficulty. 2. aid; help.

**re mark′,** 1. say; speak; comment. 2. something said in a few words; a short statement.

**re port′,** 1. an account of something seen or heard. 2. give an account of. 3. tell about.

**re quire′,** 1. need. 2. asked for. 3. order.

**re veal′,** make known; tell.

**ri dic′ u lous,** laughable; silly.

**rim,** edge.

**roy ′al,** belonging to a king or queen.

**sav′ age,** 1. wild. 2. fierce; cruel.

**scorn′ful,** mocking; making fun of.

**seal¹,** close tightly.

**seal²,** a kind of sea animal covered with fur.

**se cure′,** 1. safe. 2. firm.

**seek,** 1. try to find. 2. try; attempt.

**seize,** 1. take hold of suddenly; grasp. 2. take possession of; as, the soldiers seized the city.

**sep′ a rate,** 1. keep apart; divide. 2. go apart or in different directions.

**shack,** roughly built hut or house.

**shat′ ter,** break; break into pieces.

**sheaf,** bundle of things the same size; as, a sheaf of grain.

**shed,** a one-story building used for shelter or for storing things.

**shed,** give out. The sun shed its light.

**shield,** 1. protect; defend. 2. anything used to protect. 3. piece or armor carried on the arm to protect the body while fighting.

**si es′ ta,** a nap or short rest taken in the afternoon.

**slash,** 1. cut with a sweeping stroke of a sword, knife, whip, or ax. 2. make a slashing stroke, cut, or wound.

**slay,** kill.

**sleet,** 1. half-frozen rain. 2. to rain, snow, and hail at the same time.

**slink,** sneak; move in a guilty or ashamed manner.

**slith′ er,** slide down or along a surface.

**slope,** hillside.

**slung,** 1. threw. 2. thrown. 3. hung so as to swing loosely.

**sol′ emn,** serious; earnest.

**sought,** 1. tried to find; looked for. 2. tried; attempted.

**south′ bound,** on the way south.

**south′ ward,** toward the south.

**spank,** strike with open hand or a slipper.

**spank′ ing,** unusually fine, great, large, etc.

**square,** 1. open space in a town with streets on four sides, often planted with grass and trees. 2. a shape with four equal sides.

**square′ly,** straight; exactly.

**squint,** look with eyes partly closed.

**squirm,** wiggle; twist.

**staff,** stick; pole; rod.

**stag,** a full-grown male deer.

**stall,** a small place for selling things in a market.

**star′ tle,** 1. surprise; frighten. 2. cause to make a sudden movement.

**stern′ly,** seriously; firmly.

**stew′ ard,** person who manages things for another person.

**stroll,** walk; take a quiet walk for pleasure.

**stur′ dy,** strong.

**sub′ ject,** person under the power of another.

**sur vive′,** 1. live longer than; be alive after. 2. continue to live.

**sus pect′,** 1. think likely. 2. doubt.

**swamp,** soft wet land.

**swept,** pass swiftly; move quickly.

**tax′ i,** move over the surface of the ground or water. An airplane taxies to get into a position for rising.

**tax/i cab,** automobile that can be hired.

**tempt,** 1. cause or try to cause a person to do something. 2. appeal strongly to.

**ter/ror,** great fear.

**thick/et,** small trees or bushes growing close together.

**thong,** a narrow strip of leather.

**threat,** sign or possible cause of harm.

**threat/en,** 1. give warning of coming trouble. 2. be a cause of possible harm to.

**throng,** a great crowd.

**thrust,** 1. push with force. 2. an attack. 3. a forceful blow, cut, or stab.

**thun/der bolt,** 1. a flash of lightning and thunder that follows it. 2. something sudden or startling.

**toil,** 1. hard work. 2. to work hard. 3. move with difficulty, pain, or weariness.

**tow,** 1. pull by a rope. 2. act of towing.

**tre men/dous,** very large or great.

**tri /umph,** joy because of victory.

**trout,** a fish. A **trout rod** is a pole for catching trout.

**up/roar,** loud or confused noise.

**ut/ter,** speak; make sounds with the voice.

**vain,** 1. having too much pride. 2. **In vain** means without success.

**val/iant,** brave.

**van,** a covered truck or wagon for moving furniture, goods, etc.

**vast,** very, very large.

**ven/ture,** 1. a risky or daring deed. 2. dare. 3. dare to say, go, make, or try something dangerous.

**vex,** annoy; anger by little things.

**vic/tim,** person or animal harmed or injured.

**vi/o lent,** with strong force; as, a violent blow.

**vow,** 1. make a solemn promise. 2. a solemn promise.

**wea/sel,** small animal with a long slender body that feeds on rats, mice, and other small animals.

**wedge,** something shaped like the letter V.

**whim/per,** 1. cry with a low cry. 2. a low, whining cry.

**wil/der ness,** wild place with few people living in it.

**wil/y,** tricky; cunning; crafty; sly.

**wind/break,** a shelter from the wind.

**with drew/,** 1. drew back. 2. went away.

**with/er,** 1. fade; dry up. 2. wrinkle.

**wor/ship,** love; honor; pray to.

**yield,** give up; give in.

*Times and Places* follows *More Streets and Roads* and is designed to fit the basic reading needs at the fourth-grade level. Over 99 per cent of the words in the preceding basic books are used in this book.

The *Think-and-Do Book* to accompany *Times and Places* provides further development of word meanings and practice in recognition.

## VOCABULARY LIST

The following list contains 1060 words introduced in *Times and Places*. The following inflectional variants of known words are not counted as new words: possessives; forms made by adding *er* and *est* of comparison; forms regular except for change of *y* to *i*, the changing of *f* to *v*, the dropping of *e*, or the doubling of a consonant. Words formed by prefixing *im*, *a*, *en*, *re*, *dis*, or *un*, or by adding *s*, *es*, *d*, *ed*, *ing*, *n*, *en*, *ful*, *ish*, *ness*, *self*, *ly*, *y*, or *er* to known words are not counted. True compounds of known words, compounds formed from parts of known compounds, and parts of previously learned compounds are not counted, nor are contractions nor letters representing sounds that are not words. The following Spanish words are not counted: *muchas gracias*, *adios*, *tortillas*, and *panela*.

UNIT I
- 7 citizens
- 8 puddle
  - captain
  - share
- 9 shallow
  - object
  - wade
- 10 rule
  - burst
  - wreck
  - speed
- 11 less
  - note
  - helpless
- 12 whirl
  - bike
  - scarcely
- 13 bundles
- 14 aboard
  - strokes
  - guided
- 15 stammered
  - hi
- 16 whiskers
  - scouts
  - cost
- 17 cents
  - quarreled
  - argued
- 18 determined
  - Scoutmaster
  - honest

- 19 arrange
  - stilts
  - lemonade
- 20 audience
  - whip
  - entertained
- 21 meantime
  - arrangements
  - stunt
  - bars
- 22 patted
  - reins
  - sped
- 23 clutch
  - dragging
  - lip
  - quivered
- 24 doubled
  - collar
  - whew
- 25 pupil
  - English
  - braids
- 26 Rosa
  - familiar
  - echo
- 27 flag
  - pledge
  - allegiance
  - saluted
- 28 suggested
  - arithmetic
  - dictionary

- 29 class
  - disappointment
  - difference
- 30 prove
  - approval
  - problem
  - socks
- 31 declared
  - success
  - program
- 32 heart
  - United
  - States
- 33 county
  - Wendell
  - apiece
- 34 booths
  - Vaughans
- 35 thirty
  - nor
  - breathless
- 36 throat
  - choke
  - wailed
- 37 sobs
  - although
  - murmured
  - Hillsboro
- 38 price
  - anxious
  - weary
- 39 elbow
  - pluck
  - waist

- 40 holiday
  - business
- 41 fresh
  - quarter
- 42 actually
  - precious
- 43 Andy
  - Lincoln
  - pine
- 44 shame
  - acquainted
- 45 Phil
- 46 astonished
  - vacant
- 47 teased
- 48 gain
- 49 hopeless
  - groans
  - length
- 50 strength

UNIT II
- 51 —
- 52 west
  - Burd
  - Matthews
  - Jonathan
- 53 Ohio
  - cheap
  - quilts
- 54 harness

442

| | | | | |
|---|---|---|---|---|
| 55 | tugging | 76 | Martha | 100 | sheared | 121 | announcement |
| | lilac | | chores | | flock | | message |
| | awkward | | measured | | gracious | | curious |
| | list | 77 | fumbling | 101 | Lucy | 122 | Jerry |
| 56 | Dan | | stiff | | shawl | | cove |
| | clambered | 78 | loft | | hood | | gulls |
| | folks | | shuffling | | dismay | | ships |
| 57 | pioneers | | plunged | 102 | tufts | 123 | November |
| 58 | rough | 79 | comical | | extra | | ordinary |
| | examined | | motioning | 103 | — | | Atlantic |
| | greased | | clatter | 104 | stockings | | uniform |
| | continued | 80 | attention | 105 | dawn | 124 | doubt |
| 59 | creek | | upset | 106 | Amos | | receive |
| | grain | | mischief | | split | 125 | bottle |
| | bacon | | begun | | bend | | sailor |
| 60 | — | 81 | mentioned | | interrupted | | island |
| 61 | flowing | 82 | beneath | 107 | cannon | | radiogram |
| | westward | 83 | intended | | deck | 126 | seal |
| | glided | | attempted | | fuel | | twelfth |
| 62 | oxen | 84 | dream | | haul | | operator's |
| | soil | | gasped | 108 | Abbie | 127 | peculiar |
| | floating | 85 | Susanna | | commenced | | pebble |
| 63 | tangled | | community | | heaped | | mail |
| | canoes | | Abel | 109 | silence | | addressed |
| 64 | crops | | knitting | | viewed | 128 | tag |
| | acres | 86 | necessary | | snorting | | person |
| 65 | shingles | | reckon | 110 | hobble | 129 | Paul |
| 66 | arrival | 87 | dipper | | plume | | dumping |
| | fort | 88 | eighteen | 111 | vanished | | gravel |
| | breeze | | study | | lame | | collie |
| | thirteen | | boots | 112 | plank | 130 | bordered |
| 67 | neighborhood | 89 | coughed | 113 | pilot | | swirling |
| | needle | | contentedly | 114 | swallowed | | hire |
| | mend | | harvest | | doctor | 131 | willow |
| | darn | 90 | husking | | caused | | dad |
| 68 | borrow | | stalks | | | | youngsters |
| | lend | | fodder | | | | peppering |
| | sewing | 91 | spell | **Unit III** | | 132 | moist |
| | calico | | pronounce | | | | fistful |
| 69 | risk | | amazed | 115 | — | | scraped |
| | gathered | | correctly | 116 | radio | | commissioner |
| | humming | 92 | Abraham | | October | 133 | tons |
| | thin | | promptly | | van | | blade |
| 70 | — | | pride | | hustled | | tremendous |
| 71 | astonishment | 93 | month | 117 | Pal | | cab |
| 72 | thread | 94 | pigeon | | whined | 134 | lever |
| | weaving | | Abe | | bounded | | jaws |
| | yarn | 95 | entirely | 118 | factory | | pit |
| | praised | 96 | illness | | special | | south |
| 73 | bench | | sorrow | | mumbled | 135 | test |
| | moccasins | | afterward | | urged | | Thursday |
| 74 | pudding | 97 | Bible | 119 | snuffing | | clump |
| | valley | | crackling | | guilty | | reverse |
| | mill | 98 | soaked | | sinking | 136 | cautiously |
| | molasses | | ruined | 120 | frantically | | downward |
| 75 | depending | 99 | east | | broadcasting | | dripping |
| | | | snapping | | recognized | | |
| | | | | | amazement | | |

137 rise
chorus
job
138 dodging
dazed
feebly
drown
139 kneeling
pressed
bones
140 flight
port
Ted
June
141 co-pilot
stewardess
wire
cluster
142 swooping
propellers
taxied
143 Bert
Allen
whir
glossy
144 comfortable
Chirp
145 huddled
146 —
147 southward
148 —
149 tractor
shed
rations
January
150 heifers
grazing
chain
bale
151 weight
advised
astride
152 cuds
153 dull
nostrils
twitching
switched
154 bellowed
separate
approached
ambled
155 roots
brushwood
walnut
156 completed
munching
157 whooped

158 Henry
choose
Dr.
159 hesitated
Chicago
granted
160 —
161 Larry
fuse
162 satisfaction
motionless
shock
aid
163 gas
form
164 sputter
165 —
166 —

UNIT IV

167 —
168 wizard
Vilville
disguised
power
169 crooked
carrots
beets
squashes
170 soul
Auntie
uproar
careless
171 meanwhile
annoyed
mad
muttered
172 vexed
squinted
demanded
purposely
173 advertised
broom
ugh
174 seized
panting
fanning
175 startled
sixty
meow
176 deny
177 wrinkled
folded
jiggle
music
178 mere

179 confessed
180 till
pale
181 miserable
182 Huckabuck
Jonas
Nebraska
183 cribs
shacks
buckle
Chinese
184 —
185 spanking
brass
186 ditch
steel
clay
187 —
188 especially
natural
weep
difficult
189 persuaded
darling
tempt
appetite
190 peals
efforts
useless
glee
191 suggestions
192 royal
Marigold
kingdom
193 preferred
curtsey
194 ridiculous
195 onions
196 dachshund
roam
hooting
197 —
198 —
199 immensely
200 net
choice
nip
201 furious
202 Peramund's
remark
possessed
art
203 accomplish
loyal
204 goblin

205 shriek
gracefully
courtyard
dizzy
206 courage
sword
swept
207 guards
enchanted
vane
208 prevent
209 seeking
invitation
210 wound

UNIT V

211 —
212 York
Spanish
Roy
palm
blossoms
213 patio
base
bat
glove
peering
214 beckoned
chose
pitch
215 brim
gripped
216 avenue
reported
217 Tomas
Pedro
stall
square
rug
218 chubby
gourd
siesta
idle
thief
219 disappearance
commotion
plaza
shrug
blessed
220 Carlota
church
jogged
221 occasionally
peak
nimble
crickets
disturbed

444

222 jolt
rut
cactus
wept
stooped
223 intently
sternly
temper
strapped
224 —
225 conceal
grief
nestled
226 embracing
accusing
deserved
227 Pablo
228 Guatemala
brilliantly
peacock
opposite
229 Sylvia's
plantation
strut
230 lacy
throngs
banana
sombreros
strolled
231 selected
coffee
Roger
Friar
232 lane
233 —
234 loitered
kneading
dough
235 fragrant
jungle
ferns
236 —
237 directly
238 grasped
splendid
239 Buenos Aires
Argentina
hotel
240 traffic
241 lingered
locate
242 —
243 distressed
absent
permitted

244 Mario's
capture
pinto
level
245 midmorning
drowsy
ceased
slithered
246 chuna
target
247 ping
boleadora
weapon
thongs
tough
248 —
249 Jorge
kid
envy
Tiro's
apparently
250 midsummer
swarmed
damage
robber
251 rustled
252 —
253 Alaska
Eskimo
Tana
reindeer
254 kernels
moss
area
threaten
255 fir
permission
Cloot
bolted
256 —
257 rays
blinded
steed
desperate
balance
258 twigs
lashed
movement
heed
259 trampled
companion
flakes
blizzard
terrific
260 —
261 —
262 dainty

263 —
264 canyon
site
Terry
265 gleam
distant
rim
explore
266 trout
rod
Lewis
Drake
consent
267 fortunately
relief
timber
peaceful
268 cast
stolen
269 ranger
duty
vast
region
patrol
270 wilderness
western
brook
271 scorched
shirts
fought
spade
272 —
273 slashing
pausing
forehead
increased
274 mysterious
ventured
survive
275 pounce
weasels
prowled
preying
defend
276 dread
slim
slightest
keen
277 sneaking
fled
secure
278 arouse
terror
panic

279 squirm
force
provide
greedy
280 hollow
281 budge
crafty
shattered
282 partridge
slope
brood
toddled
283 alert
squatted
flung
flopped
injured
284 sank
falter
accustomed
285 thicket
slinking
uttered
286 shield
beak
pure
287 ants'
mound
cocoons
288 snuggled
289 colt's
war
romped
sport
290 frequently
partner
gully
mare's
nicker
291 cliff
lunged
fury
cripple
292 pain
savage
thrust
hurled
victim
293 forefeet
nudged
294 Nika
wedge
gander
northern
295 fearless
calm

445

296 rice
season
mist
upward
297 stab
departing
gradually
298 reeds
recovered
fowls
299 Frank
Gordon
vain
300 Lizzie
faithful
assist
301 sleet
bitter
freedom
advanced
302 restless
hissed
prison
303 gale
304 Smoozie
Yukon
305 ledge
Ogg
stag
306 brief
onward
drooping
pace
307 protection
cuddled
warmth
308 dismal
piercing
snarls
mingled
309 attack
mass
310 confused
moan
valiant
311 battle
312 polar
arctic
Tuffy
jagged
313 whimpering
shaggy
314 blast
buried
massive
dozed
booming

315 comfort
glimpse
316 foaming
317 toiled
318 refused
319 —
320 alligator
Santee
swamps
coiled
321 —
322 cypress
tupelo
huckleberry
323 coon
324 snake
325 tow
326 —
327 —
328 —

UNIT VII

329 famous
330 Joseph
Jacob
elder
Benjamin
jealous
331 favored
binding
sheaf
332 scornfully
fulfilled
bade
333 slay
devoured
evil
Reuben
mercy
334 caravan
camels
merchants
Egypt
335 slave
payment
blood
beloved
336 judge
trusted
labor
steward
household
337 punished
attendants
wisdom
foretold

338 seven
withered
reveal
339 famine
therefore
appoint
marveled
340 thus
pleading
341 truth
342 accepted
youth
earnestly
concerning
343 —
344 shepherd
harp
humble
345 Saul
slung
lamp
flickered
346 tune
347 friendship
staff
sling
348 Goliath
army
bragging
challenge
349 armor
helmet
spear
bid
350 belt
351 —
352 champion
rejoicing
victory
honor
353 Saint
deed
skill
subjects
worship
354 anger
vowed
pray
overcome
gallant
355 foe
aloft
sturdy
fleeing
abandoned

356 beheld
withdrew
warriors
violently
357 dealt
yield
pity
wealth
noble
358 tale
horrible
dragon
death
earthquake
359 —
360 Arc
French
Domremy
peasant
Charles
361 France
Reims
conquer
362 heaven
related
363 harsh
convinced
364 manner
leadership
365 banner
Orleans
366 —
367 slender
368 —
369 accompanied
triumph
370 —

UNIT VIII

371 —
372 Chanticleer
considered
extremely
comb
equal
373 perched
fuss
slumber
fluttering
374 lo
lurking
snout
meekly
375 cackling
insects
wallowing

376 opportunity
   wily
   regarding
377 occurred
378 flattered
   rate
   alas
   alack
379 fleet
   pursuers
   hither
   thither
380 —
381 barber's
   Garo
   advice
   observe
382 acorns
   twirl
   thumbs
   behold
   nature
383 snored
   plop
384 sore
   solemn

385 tribe
   dwelt
   midst
   hawk
   spirit
386 squaws
   wigwams
387 amusement
   eagle
   joyous
   beware
388 —
389 —
390 Rumple-
      stiltskin
   lass
   glisten
   fetch
391 punishment
   rusty
392 wisp
   dwarf
   suspected
393 spun
   trial
394 compared

395 flinging
   require
396 —
397 orchard
   sprung
398 nay
   madam
399 messenger
400 —
401 —
402 —
403 —
404 duckling
   cheep
405 hatched
406 turkey's
407 gloriously
   properly
408 improve
409 endure
   purr
410 —
411 swans
   dazzlingly
   solid
   sought

412 —
413 —
414 —
415 lacked
   neglected
416 stuttered
   bewitched
   common
417 glittered
   rapture
   rare
418 despair
419 —
420 sneeringly
   proceeded
   knight
421 attend
   further
   claimed
422 —
423 proclaimed
   realm
424 —
425 —
426 —
427 —
428 —
429 —

## ILLUSTRATORS

The pictures for this book were made by the following artists: John Merryweather (cover, pp. 1, 3, 7, 51, 94-97, 115, 122-128, 167, 211, 244-252, 263, 289-293, 320-328, 329, 371); I. B. Hazeltine (pp. 8-15, 25-49, 253-262, 264-273); Rafaello Busoni (pp. 52-93, 100-114, 217-225); Walter Oschman (pp. 116-121, 129-165, 228-237); Keith Ward (pp. 16-24, 182-184, 202-209, 381-384, 390-401); Charlotte Becker (pp. 168-179, 190-195); Christine Chisholm (pp. 196-200, 212-216, 239-241); L. M. Henderson (pp. 282-287, 294-303); Don Crane (pp. 274-279, 304-319); L. Segner (pp. 330-351, 385-389); E. Segner (pp. 404-414); Milo Winter (pp. 352-369, 416-417, 421-426); Nell Smock (pp. 372-380).

# ACKNOWLEDGMENTS

Grateful acknowledgment is made to the following authors and publishers for permission to adapt and use their copyrighted material: To Idella Purnell for "Johnny's Alligator" from "The Alligator's Tail," *Story Parade;* to Elizabeth Palmer for "A Camp in the Canyon" from "Fires Start in the Fall," *Junior World;* to Ada Campbell for "Southbound Flight," to Zelia Walters for "The Neighborhood Needle," to Hubert Evans for "Return of the Puddle Duck," to Eleanor Hammond for "Whiskers Steals the Show," to Lawrent Lee for "A New Job for a Tractor" from "Animals Must Eat," *Wee Wisdom;* to Esther Cooper for "Susanna Jane's Secret" and to Delia M. Stephenson for "Wool Gathering," *Children's Playmate Magazine;* to William H. Bunce for "Gray Wing and Nika," from "In the Wake of the Storm," *Trails,* Broadman Press; to Paul Brown for "A Wild Colt's Lesson" from *War Paint,* Charles Scribner's Sons; to Alice Gall and Fleming Crew for "Bushy Tail's Escape" from *Bushy Tail,* Oxford; to Mabel F. Rice for "Star Pupil," from "Democracy 1903 Model," *Elementary English Review;* to Dorothy C. Fisher for "Betsy Finds a Way" from *Understood Betsy,* Holt; to Iris M. Knight for "How Andy Helped His Team" from "The Race on Roller Skates," to Cornelia Meigs for "Hasty Pudding," and to Josephine E. Phillips for "Steam Comes Upriver," *Child Life;* to Enid Meadowcroft for "Going West" and "The Long Journey" from *By Wagon and Flatboat,* copyright 1938 by Thomas Y. Crowell Co., reprinted by special arrangement; to Josephine Pease for "Radio Rescue" from "What Happened to Ann," and to Allen Chaffee for "Christmas in Alaska" from "Christmas Adventure," *Children's Activities;* to Alice Dalgliesh for "Messages from the Sea" and for "A South American Visit," from "The Hollyberrys Visit South America," *Jack and Jill;* to Carol Johnstone Sharp for "The Wizard of Vilville" from "Auntie Grumble Meets the Wizard," *Just for Fun,* Rand; to Carl Sandburg for "The Huckabuck Family" from "The Huckabuck Family and How They Raised the Popcorn in Nebraska" from *Rootabaga Pigeons,* copyright 1923, Harcourt Brace and Co., Inc.; to Rose Fyleman for "The Princess Who Could Not Cry" from *The Rainbow Cat,* Doubleday; to Challis Walker for "Three and Three" reprinted by special permission of Coward-McCann, Inc., publishers, copyright 1940 by Challis Walker; to Edward Wade Devlin for "King Peramund's Wish"; to Alice E. Allen for "A Boy and His Book" from "A Little Lad of Long Ago," *Good Housekeeping;* to Alma Savage for "Smoozie the Reindeer" from *Smoozie,* Sheed; to Elizabeth Kent Tarshis for "The Red-Brimmed Hat" adapted from *The Village That Learned to Read,* Houghton; to Marian Cannon for "Adventure in Guatemala" from *Children of the Fiery Mountain,* published and copyright by E. P. Dutton and Co., Inc., New York; to Esther G. Hall for "Mario's Pet" from *Mario and the Chuna: A Boy and His Bird of the Argentine,* reprinted by special permission of the publishers, Random House. The following stories were written for exclusive use in *Times and Places:* "Steam Shovels Are Handy" by Sterling North, "When the Lights Failed" by Charles Pierce Burton, "At Home in Any Language" by Maria Martin.